Sixty Centuries of Copper

Sixty Centuries
of Copper

B Webster Smith F.G.S.

C.D.A. Publication No. 69

published by

Hutchinson of London

for the **Copper Development Association**

HUTCHINSON & CO. (*Publishers*) LTD.
178–202 Great Portland Street, London W1

London   Melbourne   Sydney
Auckland   Bombay   Toronto
Johannesburg   New York

★

First published 1965

865 - 22 813

*This book has been set in Baskerville type face,
printed in Great Britain by
Benham and Company Limited, Colchester,
and bound by
William Brendon and Son Limited,
Tiptree, Essex*

Copper Development Association
55 South Audley Street
London W.1.
Telephone: Grosvenor 8811
Telegrams: Cuda Audley London

Contents

List of Plates

7

29 Bronze stopcock installed in Hampton Court Palace in 1539
30 Late 15th Century German brass cistern
31 Celestial globe and stand, 1649
32 Bronze sculpture: Hercules wrestling with a lion
33 Macclesfield Copper Works truck token issued in 1790
34 Herschel's machine for polishing speculum
35 Faraday's induction coil—the first electrical transformer
36 A short length of the first British commercial telegraph
37 Replica of Samuel Morse's second telegraph key
38 Laying the first submarine cable from Dover to Cap Grisnez
39 Atlantic cable of 1865
40 Galvanometer which received the first signals through the Atlantic cable
41 Wilde's multipolar dynamo of 1866–7
42 World's first 3-phase a.c. turbo-generator, 1900
43 Marconi's copper induction coil and tuning inductance, 1899
44 Watson–Watt radar receiver, 1935
45 Inserting copper windings in the stator of a turbo-generator
46 Copper printed circuit
47 Copper and cadmium copper overhead conductors
48 Copper in modern undersea communications
49 Plant area of the Mufulira Mine, Zambia
50 Zambian copper mines
51 Roof of Commonwealth Institute Building, London
52 Multi-storey block of flats in a Stockholm suburb
53 Crystal Palace sports centre
54 Modern police station in Finland
55 Copper wiring cables in an aircraft hold
56 Machining a ship's propeller
57 Water-cooled copper windings for the Nimrod proton synchroton
58 Copper alloy Fourdrinier wire screen
59 Whisky stills
60 Copper in the modern car
61 20-ton copper alloy chemical vessel
62 Copper heat exchangers
63 Heat from solar energy for a Sussex pool
64 Mineral-insulated copper-sheathed cable in Birmingham
65 Copper prefabricated plumbing assembly

A list of organizations to whom acknowledgment is due for many of the photographs in this book is given on page 96.

Preface

The story of copper and its principal alloys, bronze and brass, is virtually a chronicle of human endeavour since man emerged from the Stone Age. The ubiquity of the copper metals and their contribution to every civilization since Sumeria and Pre-Dynastic Egypt gives them a unique position in the history of technology.

This book replaces a publication first issued by the Copper Development Association in 1934. Like the original work, *Copper Through the Ages*, the present volume is intended for the reader who is interested in the general history of copper mining, the development of metal-working processes and the uses of copper through the past six thousand years. The scope of the subject is so enormous that some sections have been covered only briefly, but it is felt that the book will be a useful introductory guide to students of history, particularly since the teaching of history has been broadened to embrace the origins of applied science. It should also help metallurgists, architects, industrial designers, engineers and other technologists to appreciate the part played by the copper metals in the past and recognize their potential contribution to future advances in civilization. The book traces the links between man's early uses of copper and the applications of today, and thereby outlines a continuous record of satisfactory service in which new uses for copper have been found in practically every century.

The Copper Development Association is a non-trading organization, sponsored by the copper producers and fabricators, whose aim is to encourage the correct and efficient use of copper and its alloys.

Introduction

Copper was the first metal used by man in any quantity. The earliest workers in copper soon found that it could be easily hammered into sheets and the sheets in turn worked into shapes which became more complex as their skill increased. After the introduction of bronze, a wide range of castings also became possible. Many of the illustrations in this book serve to show man's progress as a metal-worker, culminating in the priceless inheritance of the Renaissance craftsmen. But copper and its principal alloys, bronze and brass, have always been more than a means of decorative embellishment. Although iron became the basic metal of every Western civilization from Rome onwards it was the copper metals which were used when a combination of strength and durability was required. The ability to resist corrosion ensured that copper, bronze and brass remained as functional as well as decorative materials during the Middle Ages and the successive centuries through the Industrial Revolution and on to the present day.

Watt's steam engines, which ushered in the modern world, depended largely on iron and coal, with copper and its alloys making a lesser yet significant contribution, but with the subsequent development of electrical power copper proved to be the metal *par excellence*. The early decades of the 19th Century saw the foundation of the Electrical Age and thereafter the demand for copper increased tremendously. Britain was the major producer for much of the 19th Century but new mines were opened up in U.S.A., Chile, and later in Africa, until in 1911 the world's output of smelted copper for the first time exceeded a million tons per annum. With the increase in all branches of human activity which followed the Industrial Revolution new important uses were found for copper and advances in metallurgical knowledge led to the introduction of many new copper alloys.

Today more than 5 million tons of copper are produced annually and the copper metals are playing an increasingly vital part in many branches of modern technology. The ductility of copper, which led to its use for water piping in ancient Egypt, is illustrated by the countless thousands of miles of copper tube in contemporary plumbing and heating systems: the corrosion resistance of copper, which induced the Romans to use it for sheathing the roof of the Pantheon, is today verified by the thousands of copper roofs on modern buildings large and small; and the electrical conductivity of copper, which was utilized by Michael Faraday in his epoch-making experiments, remains the key to modern power generation.

These are but three of the examples outlined in this book where present applications are indissolubly linked with the past, but copper is also an essential material of the future. Solar heating, large-scale desalination of water, the linear motor are all innovations where copper will make an increasingly important contribution. The known reserves of copper ore are ample for all envisaged requirements, and continuous metallurgical research promises to provide new alloys possessing even superior properties to meet the exacting demands of the technology of the 21st Century.

1 *The Raw Material*

1. Man Becomes Metal-conscious

In the New Stone Age men first learned to live peaceably together in pastoral and agricultural communities, from which fixed settlements arose, long before they became metal-conscious. They practised agriculture, had numerous domestic implements and were skilful potters, artists and artisans in bone and certainly also in wood, when somewhere they became attracted by the shining particles of free gold in shallow river-beds. They seem to have quickly discovered that this remarkable stone, as they regarded it, could be beaten into thin plates and even fashioned into pins; and perhaps these discoveries started an inquisitive search which led them to find, first the curious lumps of native copper, although it was probably always scarce, and then the much more abundant bright green 'stone' malachite and its close blue associate azurite. Both these copper carbonates not only catch the eye but are also easily detachable from the ground. No doubt men also learned early to distinguish 'fool's gold'—the bright-yellow iron pyrites and the very similar yellow copper ore, copper pyrites —from the true gold with which they may excusably have mistaken it at first. Our knowledge of Man's earliest interest in metals in the dawn of prehistory will never be more than hypothetical, but it can be asserted more confidently that, so far as copper is concerned, these events occurred during the Fifth Millenium B.C.; hence Man's knowledge of copper must date back for at least six thousand years.

During that period two great rivers, the Euphrates and the Nile, each nourished a considerable civilization near its mouth. The former was probably of greater antiquity, since it was responsible among other things for developing the art of brick manufacture which was originally unknown in Egypt. There were two kingdoms on the lower Nile, Upper and Lower Egypt. In general terms the date of the early Sumerian civilization, which clustered around Ur and other cities, can be set at 3500 to 4000 B.C., and

Pre-Dynastic Egypt covered the same period or possibly a little later. King Menes, from whose reign all Egyptian chronology* is taken, conquered Lower Egypt and welded the two parts of the Nile people into one nation, around 3200 B.C.

A whole series of other but less important centres of early civilization in the Near and Middle East has been unearthed by archaeologists during recent decades, but they are certainly younger and their dates extremely hypothetical.

Two other major centres of mankind lay farther afield, in Hindustan and China. With immense populations and abundant agricultural resources, these civilizations also have their origins in the distant past; but the Chinese records cannot be definitely dated earlier than the Third Millenium B.C., and the civilization of India probably first began to flourish during that period. Neither appears to have derived much from the Sumerians or Egyptians, since geographical barriers, particularly in the case of China, precluded any interchange of culture.

It is against this historical background that one must try to unravel the earliest history of copper.

2. The Original Sources of Supply

The Sumerians probably drew their first supplies of copper from that treasury of metal deposits, the mountainous country round Lake Van in Armenia. Stream tin, from which bronze could be made by mixing tin ore and copper ore, was also found there; but it does not appear to have been used deliberately for many centuries. It is now apparent that a very distinct Copper Age occurred first and this was equally the case in Egypt and elsewhere.

Egypt probably drew its first supplies of copper from the native metal and from the abundant malachite in the Red Sea hills of the Eastern Desert, for the old mines lie almost on the natural trade route to the Red Sea. The Egyptians also valued turquoises and emeralds very highly, just as they did silver; and by Early Dynastic times they were receiving these precious stones from the weird desert mountain wilderness of Maghara, in south-west Sinai. This source became sufficiently famous for Sneferu, about 2800 B.C., to send an army especially to conquer the place. The expedition succeeded and, in addition, it took back some malachite, apparently by mistake; for it was named by the Egyptians 'false emerald'.

At about the same period Cyprus was receiving copper objects from Egypt and similar articles bearing cuneiform inscriptions from Sumeria,

* In this book the chronology at present adopted by the British Museum is followed.

probably sent by the ordinary desert route through Syria to the Mediterranean. Cyprus then or later developed its own copper mines which became celebrated throughout the Eastern Mediterranean.

These appear to have been the three main sources of the metal in ancient times.

3. The Name 'Copper'

In their picture-writing the Egyptians used the Ankh sign for copper. Appropriately it was also the symbol of Eternal Life; and as that still happens to be one of the main features of copper, it is used everywhere today for the metal. A long time afterwards Homer, following the Greek practice of around 1000 B.C., called the metal Chalkos; hence the Copper Age is also known as the Chalcolithic. Finally, after another thousand years had elapsed the words 'aes Cyprium' appear in Roman writings of the Early Christian Era because so much of the metal came from Cyprus. 'Copper' is the anglicized version of this Latin phrase.

4. The Spanish Mines

In the 13th Century B.C. the Phoenicians, then an enterprising and rapidly growing nation of traders and mariners, ventured into the Atlantic and established Cadiz (1240 B.C.). They soon spread a short distance inland to Huelva, where they discovered and began to work an enormous mass of cupriferous pyrite which is still the largest of its type in the world, although it is now regarded primarily as a source of sulphur. Subsequently the deposits at Rio Tinto and the neighbouring Tharsis became one of the most important sources of copper; and after the Romans had conquered Carthage in the First Punic War they occupied all Spain and seized the mines.

Originally most metalliferous mines were simply open trenches or slight excavations into hillsides. Then sloping tunnels or adits followed which provided both ingress for the miners and a way out for the product, besides an easy means of dealing with the ever-present hazard of mine water. The Romans, with their genius for engineering, improved on these methods considerably, particularly in Spain, where they reduced a hill impregnated with copper ore into a valley. Their method of breaking up the rocks was to heat them by fire and then to throw cold water over them to cause disintegration by rapid cooling. Deep shafts were dug, their walls lined with timber and water-wheels were employed for drainage; several scores of these wheels still survive. The pattern of the wheel was essentially the same as the Egyptians had already used for over two thousand years to draw irrigation water from the Nile. The Roman mines had at least thirty of these wooden wheels which revolved on bronze spindles made from an alloy of 91½ per cent copper, 6¼ per cent tin and 1¾ per cent lead. Buckets were placed on hooks at the end of each spoke. The usual number in most cases was twenty-four per wheel. A wheel was worked by slaves after the manner of a treadmill, and each raised the water about 10 ft. The miners descended into the pit by stepping stones driven into the wall, the holes for which still survive.

The Romans actually succeeded in carrying one working down to a thousand feet below the surface, some shafts having a 40-degree raise. Down below, light was provided by means of oil lamps with special wicks. By their underground workings, this remarkable people are stated to have uncovered nearly one hundred lenses of the ore.

5. Other Roman Sources of Supply

Before the creation of the Empire, the Romans were also working copper at Madjenpek in Jugoslavia, as well as mines in Asia Minor. They were in fact inveterate seekers after metals, but especially gold, silver, copper, tin and lead and at a later date also iron.

Apart from the immense deposits of cupriferous yellow ore in Spain, the principal copper ore was malachite, after the much less abundant native copper had been exhausted. The Romans may also have used some of the very noticeable greenish-blue chrysocolla (copper silicate), and perhaps a little of the very rich ore chalcocite, which is often grey or black, and sometimes soft and sooty (copper glance). The great basis of Roman supplies was Spain. The sulphide of copper found in the Spanish mines is bright yellow chalcopyrite; it contains almost equal parts of copper, sulphur and iron. It must be smelted, whereas the others can readily, although slowly, be leached out of their stony matrix. Thus, quite a long time ago the old metallurgists must have encountered some tough problems; but in this case the remarkable purity of the Spanish slags, of which enormous quantities still remain, testifies to their success.

6. The Beginnings of Bronze

The earliest definite date usually assigned to true bronze casting is about 2500 B.C., i.e. 700 years or more after copper is known to have been in use; nevertheless numerous analyses show that copper artefacts of around 3000 B.C. sometimes contain small and variable percentages of tin. These may be regarded as 'accidental bronzes'.

One of the first things that the early coppersmith must have learned was that when he hammered copper he hardened it and, conversely, by heating the object he could soften or anneal it again. Thus the unalloyed metal could be fabricated and cut in a number of different ways. But when some unknown inventor conceived the idea of deliberately adding fixed proportions of tin ore to the melt, he produced true bronze and thereby started the Bronze Age. As bronze was harder, almost equally durable and decidedly easier to cast than copper, although much more liable to fracture if not properly made, its use spread rapidly. In the Mediterranean countries bronze was not supplanted for over 2,000 years and it lasted a good many centuries longer in north-western Europe, where methods of extracting and working iron were slower to follow those of Hallstadt and Rome. Meanwhile, both bronze and copper ran side by side. Museum labels on exhibits are not to be trusted unless analyses have been made and it is only in recent years that this has been systematically undertaken.

The ancient tin was nearly always stream tin, nuggets of the ore being found in the stream gravels, perhaps in the search for gold. Tin ore occurs in Armenia, but everywhere in the world it is much rarer than copper. The main European deposits are in Saxony and Cornwall. British tin was widely famed, perhaps as far back as 1000 B.C. Knowledge of it probably reached the Continent indirectly; for as is well known there was a roundabout immigration from Spain through Ireland several hundred years at least before one can pick up the threads in England. No doubt Gaul and Kent must also have been in touch, but between Kent and Cornwall lay a vast, unbroken forest. The mining of British tin became quite an organized industry at a very early date. The metal was cast locally into ingots, and one of the probable smelters was on St. Michael's Mount, where abundant furnace scoriae from the slag have been found, and where also was situated the port of Ictis, whence traders passed into Gaul and so down to the Mediterranean.[1]*

7. Early Copper Mining in Britain

Because of its close association with tin in the mines, copper must almost certainly have been found in Cornwall at the same date, but how far it was exported, if at all, is uncertain. The Romans, for instance, could have had little need of it, since they possessed the abundant and more easily available supplies from Cyprus and Spain; while the Irish were exploiting, apparently long before the Christian Era, their own copper deposits at Avoca, in the Wicklow Mountains. No contemporary records exist and much of the data have been derived only by inference, but nevertheless it is quite

* For references to authorities, see page 92.

certain that the Celtic peoples of Britain had a good although no doubt elementary metallurgical knowledge of both metals, and most of their old workings pre-date the Roman invasion. The chief British copper mines were at Alderley Edge in Cheshire, where the easily worked malachite was abundant. There were others at Amlwch, in Anglesey, also in North Wales, Shropshire, Coniston and south-west Scotland. According to Bromehead, these were all surface workings, mere open-cast trenches and circular pits, some having once been rich in copper silicate (chrysocolla). No attempt was made to drive galleries. Probably the natives continued to work the deposits under the watchful eyes of Roman overseers; for the invaders were more interested in lead, the mining of which was an imperial preserve.

There were some small Roman copper mines at Llandudno, where an open-cast on Great Orme's Head yielded a coin of Aurelian (A.D. 270) and many more recent ones have been found in the spoil-heaps. This ore was copper carbonate. There was a large Roman mine at Llanymynech and another at Machynlleth, the former comprising a large number of cone-shaped pits and a great open-cast trench with a series of galleries opening into chambers. This place yielded coins of Antoninus and Faustina (A.D. 138). From the Scottish source comes a cake similar to those found in Wales (see below). At Marazion, Cornwall, where the causeway runs out to St. Michael's Mount, a vessel of pure copper was found buried in the marsh in 1825; it contained some thousands of brass coins of about A.D. 260.

8. Early Smelting Practice

Virtually all the ore used by the ancients was hand-picked with only the most worth-while material being taken. Originally it was probably smelted by the Sumerians in shallow pits using charcoal as the fuel. How they first derived the necessary draught to raise the temperature sufficiently to melt the ore is still a matter of speculation, but it may have been done by banking over the furnace with clay and leaving an opening directed towards the prevailing wind. Bellows were certainly known by about 2500 B.C. and some form of bellows must have been employed still earlier in order to account for the more ancient bronzes. Not until 2000 B.C. or later did these improvements reach Egypt, where hieroglyphs of that period show air being blown into the furnace through a straight tube. The bellows type reached Egypt a little later.

Long afterwards smelting furnaces acquired the shape which they essentially maintained right down to Victorian Swansea days, i.e. a small stone or brick chamber with some means of pouring or ladling out the molten metal, a hearth below, and a brick chimney, usually low and stumpy, which provided an updraught and allowed the waste gases to escape. The state of the atmosphere around such furnaces can be imagined, but both life and labour were cheap. The Romans improved on the early primitive methods, but without altering the fundamental principle; and, as already mentioned, they successfully smelted sulphide ores which would have defied the more ancient metallurgists.

In Britain there has been found in Anglesey a number of circular cakes of copper which were cast in Roman times. These cakes were 11 to 13 in. in diameter, 2 to $2\frac{1}{2}$ in. deep, and weighed from 30 to 50 lb apiece. They were formed 'by pouring the metal into a shallow tray. A comparatively smooth band which is always found on the upper surface immediately within the perimeter is due to the more rapid cooling of the metal where it touched the cold tray. The central part shows a marked rising, due to the evolution of sulphurous acid, and proves that at that time sulphide ores were being smelted. The metal must have been ladled from the furnace, not tapped. One came from Amlwch; it weighs 42 lb and is stamped "IVLS". Another is stamped "SOCIO ROMAE" '.[2]

9. Mediaeval Sources of English Copper

After the Romans abandoned Britain, little or nothing is known about metallurgy during Saxon times; but in the days of the Plantagenet kings, Britain was certainly being supplied from the Continent with its copper, mainly from Germany. During the 13th Century the valuable and very extensive copper ore at Mansfeld was being exploited and there was an equally famous mine in operation at Falun, Sweden, about 100 miles north-west of Stockholm. Not until Tudor days did English copper mining again get under way, when digging began in Cumberland and subsequently in Cornwall; German miners were imported specially for the purpose. These local developments led to the establishment of the Mines Royal at Swansea (page 44). The industry, which also involved the production of brass from calamine found in the Mendip Hills, became centred in this region; and Swansea continued to be the chief centre for smelting and refining copper from all over the world until the mid-Victorian period.

10. The Peak Years of British Copper Mining

The hey-day of British copper mining was during the earlier part of the 19th Century, when Great Britain contributed more than half of the world's output, the bulk coming from Cornwall. Industrial needs were also growing fast, so that large tonnages of the metal still had to be imported from abroad, particularly from Russia, which was then a very important producer, and from Chile. By the end of the century, however, the large, readily available quantities that had been opened up by foreign mining, coupled with the growing exhaustion of the Cornish mines and the serious trouble and expense due to the water in the workings, reduced the output of Cornish ore from 18,500 tons per annum to virtually nothing. But by 1933, the world's reputed output from smelters had risen from 291,000 tons in 1852 to about three million tons annually. The greatest single cause for this great expansion was the enormous growth of the electrical engineering industry (see Chapter 6).

During the middle of the 18th Century the quantity of British copper sold was over 700,000 tons; while from 1771 to 1838 about 5 million tons in all were produced in this country. The mine of Parys, in Anglesey, was an important producer at the former date. Copper mining had been resumed there in 1757 after a gap of centuries, and for a good many years this mine regularly produced 2,000 to 3,000 tons of copper per annum, the workings being carried down progressively to 1,050 ft below the surface. The Parys ore was a complex sulphide. With that inconsistency which has been the fate of so many mines, the supply fell away once more, but it revived again in mid-Victorian years.

Hardly any copper is now produced from British ores.

11. Older Sources of the Metal Abroad

A number of Continental countries have deposits of copper, but none can compare with the tremendous output today of the American, Canadian, Zambian, and other African mines. Some Austrian copper mines, mainly at the Mittsberg and Kitzbühl, have a long history which is stated to go right back to the Bronze Age; but there, as elsewhere in Europe, the great days of copper mining were between the 15th and 17th Centuries.

The famous mines of Mansfeld in southern Germany and the smaller one at Rammelsberg have also been worked for centuries; indeed Mansfeld goes back for at least 750 years.

The celebrated Swedish mine of Falun has been working continuously since the 13th Century; production was at its peak in the 16th and 17th Centuries, when the fumes from the smelters effectually destroyed all the vegetation in the vicinity, a state of affairs that lasted for many years. In this connexion there is a well-known story which may well be true. In 1670, a young miner named Israelson, who was engaged to be married, accidentally perished in the mine. His body was not discovered until forty-nine years later, in 1719, when it was still so perfectly preserved by the fumes of copper vitriol that his former sweetheart, then an old woman, could still recognize him.

In Norway there are many small deposits of copper. One of the most important, at Kongsberg, was being exploited by A.D. 1490, and others in Telemark by 1540.

Finland, which produced moderate quantities of the metal in the 19th Century, is now a substantial producer, despite the fact that some large and potentially very valuable deposits of copper-nickel at Petsamo were seized by Soviet Russia shortly after the last war. The Russians' own important copper mines, which are scattered along the Ural Mountains, began operations in 1700. The Soviet Union also discovered very valuable deposits during the 1930s, in Kazakstan, near the southern end of Lake Baikal; the loss of territory in 1941-2, when most of European Russia was occupied by the Germans, brought about a wonderful industrial transformation in what up till then had been a sparsely populated, semi-desert wilderness.

In the East, small Indian mines have been worked on and off for many centuries. Japanese copper records go back to at least A.D. 700, when a locally derived copper ingot was presented to the Emperor. There are quite a number of deposits of varying importance now being worked in the main island. China, too, contains numerous copper mines.

12. The Great American Expansion of Copper Mining

The major modern sources of the metal have been the two Americas and Central and Southern Africa.

The two great chains of the Andes with the high plateau of Peru between them are extraordinarily rich in metals—tin in Bolivia and silver, copper and gold in Peru and Chile, besides a number of other important economic minerals. Some of these mines were worked by the Incas, others were developed by the Spanish Conquistadores, but it was in the latter part of the 19th Century that mining first became a really large industry. Development has been continuous and new mines are being opened up today: well-known names are Cerro de Pasco, Chuquicamata, Braden, Corocoro, etc. Cerro de Pasco, situated at an altitude of 18,000 ft., is one of the highest mines in the world. At Chuquicamata, an enormous open-cast pit, which is one of the largest in the world, has been excavated: mining on a serious scale only began there in 1879 under British impulse. The Chilean ore was at first exported to Swansea, but this ceased on the later construction of local smelters. It is worth recording that in an average year between the two World Wars—say, 1927—7½ million tons of copper ore were dug out at Chuquicamata alone, which yielded 123,000 tons of copper.

The Braden mine at El Teniente, near Rancagua, Chile, is quite unique. It occupies the heavily mineralized core or plug of an extinct volcano.

The numerous large copper mines of the United States, which between them now produce roughly a million tons of copper every year, began to be exploited mainly in the 1850's. Development of the Canadian mines began chiefly at the turn of the century, and those of Zambia shortly after World War I. Many of the mine names are household words both in the industry and among investors, e.g. Roan Antelope, Mufulira, N'Changa, Anaconda, Kennecott, Chino, Miami, Sudbury, Noranda.

Whatever the metal, the life of any individual mine is generally limited, but some of the copper deposits are so extensive that they still have a long life ahead of them. Others are now merely famous names. The original Kennecott Mine, which was in Alaska, is a case in point. One of the longest-lived of the great copper mines has been Calumet and Hecla, with its fabulously rich deposits of native copper on the Keweenaw Peninsula of Michigan. Production began in 1865 and has been continuous ever since, although in recent years much of its copper has been derived by reclamation. By 1930 the annual total of copper yielded by this one mine was still next to the largest in the United States and the grand total at that date was just short of 1¾ million tons of refined copper alone.

For the great contributions towards the world's copper supplies that have been made in modern times by Canada and Zambia, see pages 76-78.

Australia and Tasmania also have valuable copper mines.

2. Copper in Ancient Times

1. The Sumerians and Chaldeans

Copper probably first came into use as the earliest non-precious metal employed by the Sumerians and Chaldeans of Mesopotamia, after they had established their thriving cities of Sumer and Accad, Ur, al'Ubaid and others, somewhere between 5,000 and 6,000 years ago. These early peoples developed considerable skill in fabricating copper and from these centres the rudiments of craftsmanship spread to the river-dwelling people of Egypt, where it continued to flourish for thousands of years long after their own civilization had degenerated.

Although the Sumerian art-forms were rather crude, many of the objects they produced were wonderfully life-like. In other respects this group of city states was at first more advanced than those of the Nile. They had a system of writing, an art which the Egyptians only acquired late in their history. They made surveys, kept exact land records, and were capable mathematicians. If we accept the chronology which is favoured at present by the British Museum, their greatest period ranged between 2800 and 2000 B.C. Bronze pots and mixing trays have been found at al'Ubaid, near Ur (c. 2600 B.C.), also silver ones of the same date, besides silver-spouted bronze jugs, saucers and drinking-vessels which were probably used for ceremonial purposes. Still earlier are some copper chisels and other tools from Ur, likewise copper razors, harpoons, cloak-pins and other small articles. Far older than any of these are some copper arrows and quivers, together with prehistoric Sumerian copper spear-heads, all of which have successfully survived the test of time.

The Sumerians were masters of sculpture and some splendid examples of their art may be seen in London. Thin copper sheets were beaten and shaped on a wooden background with a bitumen lining—a favourite design was a bull's head. These figures were attached by copper clamps to the walls of buildings, notably at al'Ubaid (c. 2800 to 3000 B.C.); sometimes they were fastened by nails or copper wires set in bitumen. To this stage belongs the magnificent Imdugud Relief (Fig. 1) which represents a lion-headed eagle holding two stags by their tails. The whole relief is of beaten copper within a copper frame and on a wooden background, the overall dimensions being 7 ft 9½ in. long and 3 ft 6 in. high. The stags' antlers, which are in high relief, were made of wrought copper and then soldered into their sockets with lead.

Even at such an early date, these people adopted the practice of burying under the foundations of buildings a record concerning the builder. Small bronze or copper figurines were likewise buried there at the same time. One such record, in the form of a copper or bronze peg 12 in. long, relates to a king of the First Dynasty at Ur. A more remarkable one shows a god holding a peg about 6 in. long; this came from the temple at Ningursu (c. 2500 B.C.).

Another proof of the indestructibility of copper is connected with a Sumerian wooden sled which was intended to run on the sands; it is picturesquely known as 'The Queen's Sledge'. This sled was drawn by two oxen wearing large copper collars, while the reins had copper studs. A Sumerian soldier who presumably marched alongside this equipage wore a copper helmet.

2. The Early Egyptians

Owing to its seclusion in the Nile Valley, coupled with its unbroken history ranging over more than five millenia, Egypt has provided more relics of its early civilization than any other country; and despite the difficulties in deciphering the hieroglyphics and the later hieratic writing, an enormous amount is known both about the country's political history and how the various classes of the people lived. The outstanding fact concerning metallurgical development is that from beginning to end of their first three thousand years, copper was the basic material and occupied a position similar to that of iron in modern technology.

From the earliest Dynasties onwards, Egypt developed a very high degree of civilization, and the exploitation of metals—copper, bronze and precious metals such as gold and silver—was an essential part of their culture. The Egyptians first made considerable improvements over the Mesopotamian technique, and then, apparently being satisfied that they had reached the summit of human excellence, they continued the same practices, century after century, so that only by reference to the king concerned can distinction be made between articles which may differ in age by a thousand years or more. This stolid conservatism is unique in the world's history. The museum visitor who for the first time actually sees a few of their abundant metal utensils, implements and other domestic articles cannot fail to be amazed by their variety, their close resemblance to patterns still in use, and their wonderful state of preservation (Fig. 3). Their excellent condition today can, to a large extent, be attributed to the dry climate, and our knowledge owes a considerable debt to their practice of burying in the tombs of the important dead complete equipment for one's needs in the next world. Thus they had model set-pieces, showing bakehouses, tanneries, brew-houses, boats, all complete with carved wooden human figures and implements which show the actual life of ancient Egypt. With these were buried the real bronze, copper and precious metal objects connected with the deceased. Despite a tremendous amount of plundering by tomb robbers throughout all the ages, much has remained for posterity.

The Egyptian coppersmith must have been a man of importance since he had to make saws, chisels, knives, hoes, adzes, dishes and trays, all out of copper or bronze, for artisans of the many trades. There still exist very serviceable early Egyptian bronze strainers and ladles; likewise tongs, some of which had their ends fashioned into the shape of human hands. Thebes has yielded beautifully preserved bronze sickle blades with very business-like serrated edges. The author once handled a copper knife, shaped like a large pen-knife and almost as sharp, although it was Pre-Dynastic, i.e. about 5,000 years old. The Egyptians even possessed bronze model bags which were carried by servants at important funerals.

3. Ancient Casting Practice

The majority of the surviving relics of early copper work are in cast form, an art which the Egyptians quickly brought to a high state of perfection. It is less easy to cast copper than bronze; but once they had learned to alloy the metal deliberately with tin, and frequently also with a little lead, the operation became much easier. The melt flow was improved, and thereafter there was no limit to their fertility of invention. In this connexion, it must be remembered that the abundant remains, which the world possesses today, are but a fraction of what once existed in Egypt, the rest having been stolen or melted down and recast into other forms.

As the fashioning and baking of clay into useful and beautiful objects was one of man's earliest discoveries and indeed may be said to come almost naturally to human fingers, clay moulds were probably employed for the earliest metal castings; a few wooden ones are also known. Open moulds no doubt came first; but as these can only produce articles that are flat on one face, the use of closed moulds must have followed soon afterwards. To cast copper successfully calls for special precautions, as it may give rise to sulphurous gases; molten copper also tends to pick up oxygen which can create unsound castings. Special openings or risers in the mould are therefore necessary, both for pouring the metal and to permit the escape of dirt and gases. The ancient coppersmith, however, was well aware of these difficulties and became very successful in overcoming them.

When a little tin or lead is added, even accidental amounts like 1 per cent, the production of sound castings becomes much easier; and this must have hastened the development of bronze as a definite alloy. Eventually their techniques became so sophisticated that bowls of almost incredible thinness, yet still perfect, were cast in this metal. At an early date great skill was acquired in fashioning double stone moulds which allowed repetition work. Sand castings, however, seem to have been less common.[3]

By one or other of these processes, all manner of things came into existence—palstaves, axes, bowls, tools of many kinds, weapons, celts, figurines, large vases and sacred vessels.

The Egyptians are commonly credited with inventing the lost wax or *cire perdue* method of casting metal. This was known too in China, but apparently only at a much later date. A. Lucas[4] describes the process:

'A model in beeswax was made of the object to be cast. This was coated with a suitable material to form the mould, probably clay or a clay mixture, and embedded in sand or earth which acted merely as a support. The hole was then heated and the wax melted and either burnt away or ran out through the hole or holes provided to receive the molten metal; the mould became hard and rigid, and ready for use. Then the molten metal was poured in and allowed to cool, after which the mould was broken away and the object given the necessary finishing touches with a chisel.'

Cire perdue provided solid castings upon which a great refinement of ornament or detail could be worked. Hollow castings were also made: these required some kind of core which was held in place either without support or by wires or other devices.

Another casting method, ideal for repetition work, was to fashion clay around an article and then remove the coating in sections. These were next thinly coated with wax and carefully reassembled. Hot wax was poured in and the mould rotated until the required thickness of solidified wax was obtained upon the inner walls. The removal of the mould left a complete wax model which could then be embedded in a suitable moulding material for treatment as described earlier. The necessary air-vents and runners for the metal were fashioned in wax whilst additional ornamentation was frequently applied to the wax model by means of dies.

By these various methods, metal shells and patterns of extreme thinness and delicacy were frequently obtained.

The process of beating thin copper sheets against a former, with or without the addition of special ornamentation or engraving, was also used by the ancient coppersmith to make a large variety of artistic objects.

4. Early Weights and Balances

The science of weighing played a considerable part in the ancient Egyptian's life, not merely in everyday trade but also in the religious ceremonies to which they were deeply committed. The balances employed were originally of simple patterns and existed even in Pre-Dynastic times, before 3200 B.C. They had two copper or silver pans suspended by cords at the ends of the centrally supported horizontal beam. Their use was chiefly restricted to the weighing of metal.

By Egyptian belief, when a man died his heart had to be weighed in the presence of Osiris, the great god of the dead. The man's soul was assumed to be represented by his heart, the weight of which must exactly balance that of a feather—the symbol of righteousness; if it did so, the soul of the deceased was taken into the company of the gods. For ordinary people, this weighing must have left heaven rather empty. Many hieroglyphics show this ceremony, together with detailed drawings of the balances employed.

Egyptian weights were originally of hard stone, carefully polished and marked; but in quite remote times cast bronze weights were also in use. A beautiful set, designed in animal forms, together with the actual balance, was buried at Amarna (c. 1450 B.C.) (Fig. 4).

Other copper weights made in Crete had the shape of little axes, each inscribed with the appropriate number of minae. The London Science Museum possesses a fine set of ancient lion bronze weights from Assyria, marked with the names of kings. These weights were cast and, if over-size, were reduced to their correct values by chiselling pieces from the base; if on the other hand they were light, the hollow body of the lion was partly filled with lead.

The ancient Chinese also used cast bronze animal weights.

5. Some Personal Objects

Hand-mirrors date from prehistoric times, when it is likely that discs of polished slate were used. The earliest known metal mirrors belong to the Egyptian 1st Dynasty (*c.* 3100 B.C.), and during the Old Kingdom, which lasted about 700 years, the characteristic shape that still exists today was first introduced. The Egyptian mirrors were originally made of copper, but this was later superseded by bronze. The faces were highly polished and ornamental ivory, glazed or painted handles were provided.

Egyptian ladies used cosmetics as much as their modern counterparts. The old blues and greens associated with eye 'make-up' were derived from copper pigments, blue being made out of azurite and a frit of silver, copper or calcium, and green from the other copper carbonate, malachite. Some of the sticks for applying eye-paint were made of bronze and are still usable after thousands of years.

Many bronze and copper razors have also survived, some of them for nearly five thousand years. The earliest razors were simply scraping tools made of copper with a hardened and sharpened edge. Here again bronze was subsequently introduced. By 2000 B.C. the razor had attained the shape of a small axe with a very fine blade, and a few centuries later the Nile dwellers had even invented a rotating type of razor, which was held between the finger and thumb and used in rotary motion. Hair-tweezers were employed even in prehistoric times, and some of these too are still in existence.

One remarkable object now in the British Museum is a small but wonderfully designed toilet implement of the XVIIIth Dynasty (1450 B.C.); it comprises a bronze casting of a man riding a horse, in the very attitude of a modern show-jumper taking a fence!

The ancient Egyptians never developed a system of coinage. Most of their exchanges appear to have been by barter, but they also used pieces of gold, silver and copper as media of exchange—sometimes with a special design.

The wealth of articles found at Amarna include bronze branding-irons of about 1370 B.C. for marking cattle. Even older are some bronze implements for cutting out linen; these had handles or other ornamentation in the form of a goat.

6. Glazes and Glass

It has been suggested that the idea of glazing first came from slags of the early metal smelters. Many of the beautiful Egyptian glazes in fact owed their richest colours to inclusions of powdered copper. Greenish-blue glazed ware was made even by the Pre-Dynastic people and during the next 1500 years this art reached a high degree of excellence, culminating in fine blue glazed ware for inlay and decoration. There were also glazed tiles, likewise coloured glass stones for finger-rings, earrings and other trinkets.

In some cases the blue hues were obtained by a mixture of copper and soda, whilst the brilliant ruby red was derived, as it is still, from cuprous oxide; specimens from Amarna contained as much as 12 per cent of this compound.

According to the eminent Egyptologist, Sir Flinders Petrie, Egyptian glassmaking techniques were as follows: 'The manufacture of glass is shown by examples in the XVIIIth Dynasty. The blue or green colour was made by fritting together silica, lime, alkaline carbonate and copper carbonate; the latter varied from 3 per cent in delicate blues to 20 per cent in deep purple blues. The silica was needed quite free from iron in order to get the rich blues, and was obtained from calcined quartz pebbles; ordinary sand will only make a green frit. These materials were heated in pans in the furnace so as to combine in a pasty, half-fused condition. The coloured frit thus formed was used as paint in a wet state, and also used to dissolve in glass or to fuse over a surface in glazing. An entirely clear, colourless glass was made in the XVIIIth Dynasty, but coloured glass was mainly used. After fusing a pan full of coloured glass, it was sampled by taking pinches out with tongs; when perfectly combined it was left to cool in the pan, as with modern optical glass. When cold, the pan was chipped away and the cake of glass broken up into convenient pieces. A broken lump would then be heated to softness in the furnace, rolled out under a bar of metal held diagonally across the roll, and when reduced to a rod of $\frac{1}{4}$ in. thickness, it was heated and pulled out into even rods of about $\frac{1}{8}$ in. thick. These were used to wind round glass vases, to form lips, handles, etc., and to twist together for spiral patterns. Glass tube was similarly drawn out. Beads were made by winding thin threads of glass on copper wires and the greater contraction of the copper freed the bead when cold.'[5]

Again, 'Large tiles a foot in length were glazed completely all over and used to glaze the walls of a room; they were retained in place by deep dovetails and ties of copper wire. . . . A kind of visiting card was also made in glaze, with the figure of a man and his titles to present in temples which he visited; and glazed ornaments and toggles for fastening dresses were common. . . . A piece of a glazed tile and part of a glazed vase exist which have the royal titles and name of Menes, originally in violet inlay in green glaze (3200 B.C.).'[6]

Long afterwards the Assyrians also used copper silicate to give a blue colour to their glazed bricks.

7. The Temples

Copper and bronze lent dignity and added to the other colours which adorned the great temples. A particular feature of these temples was the obelisks on either side of the entrance. One of these was 100 ft long, beautifully shaped and polished out of a single piece of red granite. Bronze caps were used to ornament and protect the pyramidal summits of these huge stelae. Some of the temples certainly had bronze doors, although none has survived the re-melting; but there still exists an Egyptian temple door-hinge in bronze, besides rectilinear bronze door-holders and an inscribed bronze door plate of Amenophis III (1380 B.C.). Bronze keys, chains and bolts, but of a later date, are also among the treasures of European museums.

The statues of the Pharaohs and their queens, although formalized in attitude, show an extraordinarily wide range in the representation of the head. They were mostly of granite or the much finer-grained, dark volcanic stone. There are few more outstanding pieces of sculpture anywhere than the tremendous outstretched arm with its clenched fist, all in polished red granite, of the greatest Egyptian king, Thothmes III, which is now in the British Museum. Copper or bronze statues are rare, but two famous ones, of Pepi I and his son Pepi II, may have been cast by the *cire perdue* technique.

In a nation so devoted to ritual their most useful metal naturally played its part in the temples. Many metal ritual objects have been preserved, including copper censers and lids now 4,500 years old, and ceremonial offering-tables on metal stands with little copper cups that might have been made only yesterday.

8. Music and Dancing

The Egyptians loved music and dancing, and many of their pictures show feasts with the musicians and dancers, but only a few of their instruments have been preserved. Some wooden flutes of a late date had bronze mouth-pieces and ends; and bronze cymbals with their original linen cords have also survived. One great treasure is the famous copper trumpet which was found in the tomb of Tut-ankh-Amen, 1430 B.C.

9. Other Near Eastern Nations Also Used Copper

During the last few decades archaeologists have been engaged in opening up ancient rubbish-mounds and sites throughout the Near East, from Crete and the Greek islands across Turkey and Iran to the Indus; and they have made some extraordinary discoveries, disclosing the remains of many an ancient civilization, such as at Hissarlik, in Azerbaijan, and elsewhere. In addition, already famous sites such as Mycenae, Minos and old Jerusalem have been further examined. Most of the new discoveries relate to thriving but hitherto little-known towns and buildings in which many bronze or copper articles have been found. Most of them range from between 2000 B.C. and 1000 B.C. They serve to show the universal demand for these metals and often, too, a high and hitherto unsuspected degree of skill in working them. The coppersmith's art reached a particularly high level at Urardhu, south-east of Lake Van, whose people were celebrated for their skill in metal-working many hundreds of years before the Roman legionaries penetrated to that part of the world. Some wonderfully lifelike bronze bulls, which were made by the Urardhu people, can now be seen in a London museum. In Western Iran, not very far away from Lake Van, bronze horse-trappings have been found, including the rein-ring and bits together with harness-mending pins.

10. King Solomon's Temple

The antiquity of the Jews is much less than is commonly imagined, for the Egyptians were a very old mature nation, steeped in tradition, long before they conquered and enslaved the Jewish people. Nevertheless, Solomon was king around 1000 B.C. The twin pillars that once stood before the porch of Solomon's Temple at Jerusalem were of bronze. They were about 3 in. thick, 6 ft in diameter, and more than 26 ft high. At their summits rose elaborate bronze capitals 7½ ft high. Within this temple stood the celebrated 'Bronze Sea', a circular bronze tank holding more than 16,000 gallons which rested upon the backs of twelve bronze bulls.

11. Copper and Bronze in Ancient China

Several thousand years before the Christian era a flourishing civilization existed in Hindustan, and sites on the Indus are now being systematically examined. Farther east, in China, the general use of metals dates back to at least 2000 B.C., and by 1200 B.C. bronze foundrywork had reached a high state of perfection. There exist whole series of magnificently ornamented bronze vessels of that time, both useful and ceremonial; some are illustrated in Figs. 8 and 9.

The Chinese adhered to fixed percentages of tin in their bronzes, and they also freely added a quantity of lead. An ancient book entitled *K'ao kung chi* mentions copper as the metal *par excellence*. It gives the following analyses of alloys for various purposes:

Cauldrons and bells:	5 parts of copper to 1 of tin
Axes:	4 ,, ,, ,, ,, 1 ,, ,,
Halberds and spears:	3 ,, ,, ,, ,, 1 ,, ,,
Swords and knives:	2 ,, ,, ,, ,, 1 ,, ,,
Erasing knives and arrows:	3 ,, ,, ,, ,, 2 ,, ,,
Mirrors and specula:	1 ,, ,, ,, ,, 1 ,, ,,

In the earlier types of Chinese metalwork the ornamentation on the surface was an integral part of the casting; but by the 7th Century B.C. such objects were often engraved and then inlaid very skilfully with gold, silver, turquoises and other precious stones.

Although the Chinese claim to have used coins for money thousands of years before the Christian Era, none has been found which is earlier than the 3rd Century B.C. By then their well-known 'cash' had been introduced; this comprised copper discs with square holes in the centre through which string was threaded. This type of coinage lasted in China right down to the 20th Century.

1. Copper-relief found at Al'Ubaid, near Ur, dating from about 3100 B.C. Known as the Imdugud Relief, it is entirely of copper and shows a lion-headed eagle holding two stags by their tails.

2. A bronze kneeling figure of Tuthmosis IV, 18th Dynasty *circa* 1425 B.C.—one of the many Egyptian bronzes to be seen in the British Museum.

3. The tombs of the Egyptians have yielded many examples of copper craftwork. The copper altar and vessels shown above date from the 6th Dynasty and are from the tomb of the priest, Idy.

4. A set of Egyptian bronze animal weights, *circa* 1450 B.C.

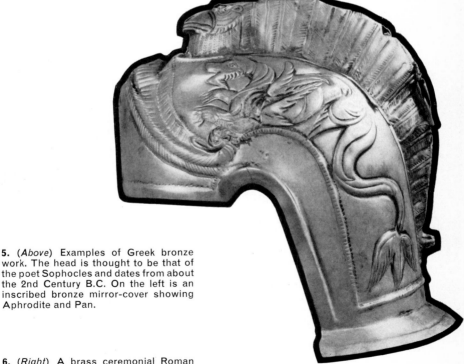

5. (*Above*) Examples of Greek bronze work. The head is thought to be that of the poet Sophocles and dates from about the 2nd Century B.C. On the left is an inscribed bronze mirror-cover showing Aphrodite and Pan.

6. (*Right*) A brass ceremonial Roman parade helmet recovered from the River Wensum, Norfolk, September 1947.

7. A Chinese bronze axe-head from the Shang Dynasty, 12th Century B.C.

8. The shape of this Chinese bronze kettle is not unlike its modern counterpart. It is 10¾ in. high and was originally inlaid with gold and silver.

9. Now in the possession of the Royal Ontario Museum, Canada, these copper knives and spearheads are believed to date from around 3000 B.C.

10. A copper flower-pot decorated with Cloisonné enamel from the Ming Dynasty, A.D. 1368–1644—the zenith of Chinese craftsmanship.

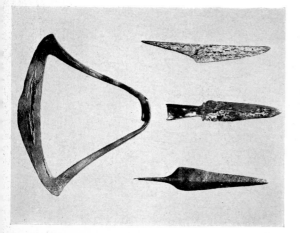

11. The Great Buddha of Kamakura, situated about forty miles south-west of Tokyo, is a major tourist attraction today. It was cast in bronze in A.D. 1252.

12. Many hundreds of statues of Indian deities were cast in copper and bronze—this typical example shows the goddess Devi.

13. West African Benin bronze—early 16th Century A.D.—representing a memorial head which was placed on an altar dedicated to a dead Queen.

14. Part of a West African bronze leopard originally used for altar decoration.

15. Bronze candlestick from Lorraine—latter half of the 12th Century, height 7½ in. Both objects on this page can be seen in the Victoria and Albert Museum, London.

16. A brass ewer in the form of a lion—Flemish, 13th or 14th Century A.D., height 10 in.

3. Copper and Bronze in Ancient Greece and Rome

1. The Ever-changing Pattern

As civilization progresses new materials are developed but older ones are rarely discarded; rather are they used more for specialized purposes, particularly if they are comparatively scarce. This was the fate of bronze in Rome, after the introduction of iron smelting about 600 to 700 B.C. In this case the durability of copper and its principal alloy, bronze, and their attractive appearance, ensured continuing use of both metals although on a more limited scale. Moreover, the discovery soon afterwards of a new copper alloy, brass, opened up endless fresh opportunities for the copper-smith's art.

2. The Greek Sculptures

The Greeks, with their exquisitely fine sense of aesthetic appreciation, their knowledge of perspective and movement and drapery, and their awareness of anatomy, brought the fine arts to a pitch that subsequent nations have copied but never surpassed. They excelled particularly in sculpture, and as several kinds of fine marble were abundant, they made great use of that medium; but they also used bronze to a considerable degree, although most of their larger pieces were melted down in later centuries because of their monetary value.

One of their most famous works, which stood in the Parthenon, was a colossal statue of the patron goddess of the city, Athene. This was 40 ft high, sculptured by the immortal Phidias, and entirely of gold and ivory. Outside the temple were two other colossal statues of Athene, both in bronze. One stood on the corner of the Acropolis and was visible far out to sea.

One of the Seven Wonders of the Ancient World, the celebrated Colossus at Rhodes, was the largest of many colossal statues of the Sun-god upon the island; it stood 105 ft high and consisted entirely of bronze. It was made by Chares of Lindus, one of the most famous bronze sculptors of antiquity, and took twelve years to manufacture and erect (292 to 280 B.C.). Pliny, who may have seen it, says that the fingers were larger than most statues and few people could embrace its thumb. It cost 300 talents and stood at the entrance to the harbour, but probably not across it as is commonly shown in pictures. After fifty-six years it was overthrown and broken to pieces by an earthquake; and there the remains lay for more than nine hundred years, until they were sold by one of the Arab Khalifs to a Jew of Emessa who carried them away on 900 camels (A.D. 672). Hence Scaliger calculated the weight of the bronze as 700,000 lb. Considering the mechanical difficulties both of modelling and of casting so large a statue, the nicety required to fit together the separate pieces in which it must necessarily have been cast, and the skill needed to adjust its proportions according to the laws of optics and to adapt the whole style of the composition to its enormous size, we must assign to Chares a high position as an inventor in his art.[7]

Lysippus, the master of Chares, was still more famous. Beginning as an ordinary workman in bronze, he decided that his statues, in which he specialized, must be absolutely natural in attitude and expression. He made the enormous number of 1,500 statues, nearly all bronze; 'in consequence of which', wrote his biographer with bitter irony a hundred years ago, 'none of them remain', although many are known from coins.

3. The Smaller Articles

The Greeks also used their skill to produce exquisite little figures only a few inches high, such as the supports or handles for bowls, the handles of mirrors and caskets, armour and a hundred other items.

The celebrated Siris bronzes, which are now in London, are in this category. They comprised the shoulder-plates of a warrior's armour, having two small lions at the top, probably with rings for fastening to the cuirass. Each figure shows a warrior defeating an Amazon. Like many other bronzes in high relief, they were beaten out of sheets by repoussé work. The face of the plate was laid against some yielding material such as pitch, and the back beaten into shape by the appropriate tools. The plate was then turned over and the ornamentation finished off by chisels, etc. In many cases the bronze sheet was exceedingly thin and it must have required extraordinary patience, judgment and skill not to pierce it accidentally. Other bronze reliefs were cast in the solid.

It was a Greek practice to deposit small votive offerings, which were often of metal, both in the temples and in private shrines, and many have been preserved. One of these portrays a contest between an Amazon and a warrior, with the Amazon in this case the victor. Mythological subjects are common on these bronzes; but the fine native sense of ridicule was never far away; thus a piece from Naples (which was one of the early Greek colonies) shows Eros playing with a goose.

Also from Italy, on the Volturno, comes a figure of Aphrodite, who was a favourite subject for many bronzes. The bronze was cast upon an iron core, with the forearms cast separately and afterwards riveted on. There is still extant an Aphrodite bronze of the 4th Century B.C., in which 'the eyes were inlaid with some material indicating their natural colour, such as a vitreous paste, ivory and ebony or gems'.[8] Of a much later date is a very fine bronze head of the Roman emperor Augustus, which was found by Garstang in 1910 in the Sudan; this had inlaid eyeballs perfectly preserved.

4. Greek Armour, Ships and Miscellanea

Armour, weapons, tools, vases, cauldrons (sometimes with bronze tripods), beautiful ornamental mirrors of many kinds, razors, bracelets and brooches in copper or bronze were common features of the ancient Greek world. The splendid sculptures in stone, such as the Pediment of the Parthenon, were not only painted but also had detailed parts, like the horses' reins and harness made of bronze and cunningly inserted. The temples themselves were of stone, usually with stone or wooden roofs; but copper was also used for temple roofs as far back as Hesiod's day (about 650 B.C.).

When at the height of their power, the Athenians had by far the largest navy in the world. Their warships or triremes, each of which was propelled by 150 oarsmen, were long and relatively narrow. Like all ships of this design their strength depended on strong wooden beams, known as walings, which ran fore and aft and terminated at the fore end in a battering-ram sheathed in bronze. For many centuries Mediterranean ships also carried a large swan-neck at the stern; this too was sheathed in bronze. Swords, spears, arrows and other weapons were all made of bronze, which became the established material for this purpose all over the world. In the later chariots, which were normally lightly constructed, it was the practice of some nations to attach a bronze scythe or sickle to the axle.

The Greeks mainly employed a silver coinage. It was beautifully minted, and bronze dies were used exclusively.

5. The Etruscans

Engraving as a form of ornamentation does not appear to have appealed very much to the Greeks, even in the colonies known as Magna Graecia in Italy. However, the Etruscans, a cultured people who were very uncomfortable neighbours of Rome, then a rising power, specialized in this art. They were adept at chiselling designs and filling in the grooves with gilding, etc. Their heritage includes a priceless range of interesting bronze objects. One notable example, on view in London, represents a racing scene in relief with two horsemen riding over a fellow-competitor who had fallen.

6. Copper in Roman Buildings

In pure art the Romans merely copied the Greeks, but they developed bronze casting techniques that were capable of producing every facial detail on their bronze figures. Heads of these figures have been found in the temples, in river mud and in other localities where anything but bronze or copper would have corroded long ago.

As an essentially practical nation, the Romans were great builders and engineers. Neither time nor siege, nor natural catastrophes, has destroyed their solid stonework. Roman stone structures were not infrequently held together by copper or bronze ties and clamps and they made more use than the Greeks of copper and bronze in their important buildings: but here again the hands of the spoiler and the pockets of the needy have melted down most of the evidence.

The finest surviving architectural work of this type is the Pantheon at Rome, an immense circular temple 143 ft in diameter which is surmounted by a dome of 140 ft. The dome had an open hole, or cella, 30 ft across at its apex which provided the only light to the interior. This dome was originally covered with copper plates with an outside covering of copper or bronze tiles; but only the central ring now remains. The tiles were stolen by Constans II in A.D. 663, and carried off to Constantinople, but were captured by the Saracens *en route*. Almost a thousand years afterwards Pope Urban VIII removed the copper plates from the roof, an act which yielded him 200 tons of copper sheets, in addition to four tons of copper nails.

During the great days of the Early Empire, when the wealth of the world lay at their feet, the Romans spared nothing in the way of luxury or decoration. Their temples had bronze doors and the vestibules were sometimes enclosed by bronze grilles; but only the great bronze doors of the Pantheon still remain unmelted.

7. Roman Water Supply

In the Mediterranean countries, all of which have a long dry season and rocks largely of porous limestone, the regular supply of water to cities and villages, as well as for irrigation, has always been a problem. The Romans excelled in this branch of engineering and their great aqueducts, whether underground or spanning deep valleys, are among the most striking relics of antiquity.

Rome itself was supplied by nine great stone aqueducts which were subsequently increased to eleven. Three of them were more than fifty miles long. They were lined with cement and were up to 3 or 4 ft wide; although they were in fact tunnels, they were high enough for a man to pass through them. The distribution of the water to fountains and dwellings from the large reservoirs which were fed by these aqueducts was sometimes by means of lead pipes and sometimes by wood; but as early as 27 B.C. the architect Vitruvius pointed out the danger to health from lead poisoning; and in his book *De Architectura* he adds, 'Therefore it seems that water should not be brought in lead pipes if we desire to have it wholesome'.[9] Bronze was too expensive at that time for piping; but the Romans, who were complete masters of all matters relating to pumping, etc., frequently used copper or bronze pumps, stopcocks, valves and other fittings.

8. The Beginnings of Brass

The Romans were the first to use brass on any significant scale, although the Greeks were well acquainted with it in Aristotle's time (*c.* 330 B.C.). They knew it as 'oreichalcos', a brilliant-and-white copper, which was made by mixing tin and copper with a special earth called 'calmia' that came originally from the shores of the Black Sea. Pure zinc was not known until quite modern times, the ore employed being calamine which is an impure zinc carbonate rich in silica. The earliest brass was made by mixing ground calamine ore with copper and heating the mixture in a crucible. The heat applied was sufficient to reduce the zinc to the metallic state but not to melt the copper. The vapour from the zinc, however, permeated the copper and formed brass which was then melted.[10]

In historical records, the word 'brass', like 'bronze', must not be taken too literally, but should be interpreted according to the known metallurgy of the times. Brass is frequently mentioned in the English version of the Bible, although so far as the Old Testament is concerned, the word probably referred to copper or bronze. In the New Testament, 'chalkos' means copper or bronze.

Some Roman armour, particularly the helmets worn on ceremonial occasions, was made of brass (Fig. 5). A large number of fine specimens of these helmets still survive. Spears and swords, daggers and palstaves, were originally of bronze, but later for weapons the Romans turned entirely to iron.

The Romans also used brass for brooches (fibulae), personal ornaments and for decorative metalwork. The alloys employed contained from 11 to 28 per cent of zinc, and the Romans clearly knew the value of different grades of brass for different purposes. The quality specified for delicate decorative work, for instance, had to be very ductile and of a good colour; and the Roman mixture contained about 18 per cent of zinc and 80 per cent of copper, i.e. it was about the same as the modern 'gilding metal' so widely used today for imitation gold jewellery.

9. The Roman Coinage

The Greeks used only a few copper coins, but the Romans had a large variety of copper money. The Roman *As* probably signified originally 1 lb weight of uncoined copper. It was divided into twelve ounces, the first six of which were represented by copper coins. The earliest Roman currency comprised copper or bronze cast bricks, upon which was stamped the figure of an ox. This money was weighed—splendid specimens of their early bronze balances still survive—and it may be that copper coins resulted from the necessity of having pieces of uniform size, thickness and weight in order to provide accurate small change. The earliest Roman copper coins were not struck, but were cast in stone moulds. Subsequently the impression, a two-headed Janus on one side and the prow of a ship on the other, was struck on the plain discs, which were placed on an anvil. In Imperial times the head of the reigning Caesar generally appeared on the face of Roman coins.

10. Musical Instruments

In the long and involved history of musical instruments, copper and bronze have been featured since ancient times. Many examples of an ancient bronze horn, the large Danish lur, have been found in peat bogs, etc., where they were buried up to 2,700 years ago. Some of these instruments, which can still be played, were shown in London a few years ago.

The Romans had copper alloy horns and bronze trumpets called buccinas. The latter were mainly military instruments and had only one or two notes, like most of the other trumpets of that period. The buccina was employed to sound the morning and evening watches, as well as at funerals. It was also sounded on festive occasions to announce the sitting down at the table and the rising (for those who could rise) afterwards.

Another instrument which the Romans developed at least two thousand years ago was the organ. One of these early organs is known to have had ten bronze pipes.

11. The Barbarian Fringe

The term 'Barbarian' was applied indiscriminately by the Greeks and Romans to all who resided outside the boundaries of their Empires. In its purest sense the word meant either non-Greek or non-Roman and was applied to the Gauls, the Goths, the Dacians, and, farther away, the Scythians, Danes, Northmen, Celts and Britons. But although these tribes were still in a semi-pastoral state, they had a civilization of their own and provide us today with by far the most interesting relics of the Bronze Age,[11] ranging from long before 1000 B.C. down to Early Christian Days. Many of these relics have been recovered from kitchen middens and bogs, from the long barrows and round barrows in which some tribes buried their dead, and from chance discoveries at river fords and similar places. Occasionally discoveries have been made of 'hoards' left by an old bronze-founder and implements of many kinds have been collected in great numbers—celts, palstaves, spear-heads, arrow tips, tools of various kinds, shields, buckets, ornaments, even jewellery.

After the discovery of iron-smelting and working, which has been traced to Hallstadt, Austria, around about 600 B.C., that metal steadily grew in importance even among the barbarians, until at last it predominated; but for many centuries the two metals were used more or less in equal proportions. Much of the earliest iron work, however, has perished through being transformed into shapeless rust, whereas the copper and bronze have survived to augment modern knowledge of the art and craftwork of the ancient world.

4. Copper in the Middle Ages

1. The Background

Ruined by its own prosperity and universal dominion, the later Roman Empire fell into inevitable decline. Under the growing onslaughts of the northern barbarians, the weak and degenerate Western Empire tumbled into ruins and carried the wreckage of its civilization with it. For nearly a thousand years the world witnessed the slow transformation of the newcomers from forest tribes and raiding nomads into organized states, who eventually became the dominant powers of the Middle Ages—the French, Germans, Burgundians, Lombards, Anglo-Saxons, Danes and Northmen. It was the Normans, the strong and able successors of the Northmen who had settled in Northern France, who eventually established their customs and feudalism over most of Europe from Britain to the southernmost tip of Sicily and even into the Near East. Only the Church continued to grow and to flourish throughout this long period, firmly held together by monasticism, and retaining within its bosom many relics of the old learning and the seeds of many trades. For the monks were not mere saints, but very practical people, with a keen eye for their own interests, a subtlety of mind that was quite beyond the mental range of their nominal rulers, a genius for picking out the best sites and acquiring the most valuable lands for their abbeys, and the highest talent in church building that the world has seen. It is amusing to note how the Venerable Bede, after upbraiding a drunken monk for his misbehaviour, excused him because he was a first-class smith!

Such were the Middle Ages, a time when bronze had given place very largely to iron, when agriculture was paramount, when internecine wars were common, and industries few and comparatively simple.

In Britain the Anglo-Saxons, who were skilled woodworkers, especially in oak, and also highly skilled blacksmiths, took little account of metals other than gold, silver and iron. During many centuries their basic currency was the silver penny, although a few copper coins were occasionally struck, notably in Mercia during the 8th Century. Inevitably in this period the art of coppersmithing declined, even on the Continent.

The impact of the Norman Conquest profoundly altered the English way of life. The feudal system, with its highly organized scale of duties; the institution of settled King's Laws and their savage enforcement; and the acquisition of power by individual barons, around whose castles clustered all the people who sought their protection, encouraged the growth of towns and a middle class of traders and guildsmen who steadily forced their way to independence. The tremendous impact of the Mediaeval Church, with all its panoply of ceremony, colour and wealth, encouraged certain trades and stimulated arts and crafts though not learning. Nevertheless for a long time England depended mainly upon wool, beef and mutton, and drew most of her metals from the Continent. Brass, in particular, was regarded with great favour in this country, and was known for a long time under its French name of 'Latten'.

2. Monumental Brasses

Brass was used in Britain for many purposes, but especially for church monuments. About 10,000 monumental brasses of varying antiquity still exist in church floors all over England. There is a notable example at Stoke d'Abernon, where Sir John d'Aubernoun has lain almost seven hundred years (since 1277), so that countless worshippers must have walked over his grave during the intervening centuries without destroying his memorial.

The old monumental brasses were thick plates, let into the floor above the grave, the stone being incised so as to maintain a level surface. On the plate was inscribed an effigy of the deceased which usually showed his dress or armour, the figure of his wife, and often details of his life. Most of these plates were rectangular, with or without a frame bearing an inscription in Gothic characters; many were also carved into outlines of the figures of the deceased. Occasionally the engraved lines were filled in with coloured enamels. Monumental brasses probably first came into vogue in the Low Countries, but many of the Continental memorials were dug up and melted.

There were once a great many monumental brasses in Westminster Abbey, but according to Gilbert Scott, 'owing to the value of the material most of these have been stolen and only a dozen remain'.[12]

Brass, in fact, was regarded as so valuable that many of these plates were dug up, turned over, and the reverse side used for another subject.

One of these palimpsests, after being first used in Staffordshire in 1447, was treated in this way almost a century later, to record in 1538 the first deceased's eight sons and five daughters.

Even in 1644 there is an entry in the Parish Book of St. Margaret's, Westminster, which reads '£1.13.4 received for 29 lb of fine brass and 96 lb of coarse brass taken from sundrie tombs'.[13]

3. The Mediaeval Bell-founders

The casting of bells is an art for which England has long been renowned. Billiter Street (formerly Bellyeter Street) in London takes its name from the bell-founders who once worked there. British bells are and always have been sand-castings. One English bronze bell, cast in 1380, is still in use, but the record of bell manufacture goes back much earlier. Roman bells were cast from Campanian brass, whence comes the word 'campanile' for a bell-tower. Most bells, however, are of bell metal—a special bronze. Bells of Western countries generally have 4 parts of copper to 1 of tin, or even 13 to 4; whereas in China and Japan, right down to the present day, the proportions have been maintained at 5 to 1, which gives the bell a more sombre tone.

Bells of a considerable size were used in England as early as the 6th Century, and even earlier in Ireland, to summon people to prayer. One of the earliest English records of bell founding is an entry at Battle Abbey, Sussex, relating to its tenant, 'One Aedric who cast bells' (11th Century). It is also recorded that four bells for the Chapel at Windsor Castle were made from material left over from the casting of the Great Bell of Westminster. The Westminster Bell arose from an agreement between King Henry VII and the famous Abbot Islip, in which the abbot solemnly promised 'to cause a great bell in the said monastery solemnly and distinctly to be knolled fourtie strokes' before the chantry masses. This bell was originally cast in 1430. It still exists, but has since been twice recast. It weighs about 34 cwt, and is 4 ft 7 in. wide and 3 ft 5 in. high.[14] There is a stained glass in a window of York Minster (c. A.D. 1200) which depicts two bell-makers at work.

One could fill a volume about bells; for, as one old abbot had inscribed in monkish Latin upon a church bell long ago:

'I mourn for death, I break the lightning, I fix the Sabbath, I rouse the lazy, I scatter the winds, I appease the cruel.'

At a later date, he might have added, 'I announce the wedding, I shout for victory, I call the assembly to order' and many another duty.

4. Mediaeval Ordnance

The experience gained through the handling of comparatively large bronze castings must have proved of much value when the discovery of gunpowder in Europe brought cannon into use. Cannon appear to have been first cast in iron and were originally quite small. Very early bronze guns are also known and the weapons, which were used by Edward III at Cambrai and Crecy, may possibly have led to the industry becoming established in England soon afterwards. Similar guns were used by the German armies in Italy even earlier, at the siege of Cividale in 1331.

Probably the first recorded instance of brass guns being manufactured in England was in 1385, when three brass cannon are stated to have been made by the Sheriff of Cumberland. From these small beginnings has grown the modern armaments industry which, during the two world wars in the 20th Century, consumed immense quantities of copper, brass and many special copper alloys, primarily for shell and cartridge cases.

Most of the early cannon were breech-loaders. They were cast in two pieces, the barrel being attached after loading to the chamber which contained the charge. Later they were cast in one piece and finished by boring; but they were never very accurate even in Nelson's day, hence the famous order, 'Reserve your fire until you can see the buttons on the Frenchmen's coats'.

As soon as the effect of the early guns was appreciated their size grew, particularly during the 15th Century, There stands on Tower Green, London, a Turkish breech-loading gun made of bronze in two parts which were screwed together after loading. This great weapon was made in 1464 for Sultan Muhammed Khan. It was one of forty-two similar guns mounted at the Dardanelles, twenty-two on the north shore and twenty on the south. Each gun weighed about 18 tons, had a bore of 25 in. and fired a round stone ball weighing about 6 cwt. Even after three hundred years, in 1807, the battery was employed with great effect against a British squadron and caused considerable losses, one shot alone killing and wounding sixty men.

The English ordnance founders were fully occupied during early Tudor times; but when Henry VIII decided to improve and enlarge the Navy he was constantly irritated by delays in the supply of cannon from abroad. England's dependence upon foreign supplies of copper, moreover, caused much uneasiness; hence both Henry and his successors encouraged mining of English copper, also of tin and calamine, with the consequences already noted. Elizabeth I always had a strong sense of strengthening her defences. Her great and farseeing Secretary of State, Cecil, was also personally involved in the development of the two joint stock companies, the Mines Royal and the Mineral Battery Company, both politically and financially.

In recent years quite a number of bronze cannon from this period have been retrieved from the sea-bed, covered in weeds and barnacles, but otherwise little worse for their centuries of immersion in salt water. One famous old ship, the *Mary Rose*, sank off Spithead in 1545. The recovery of her armament showed that she carried four kinds of brass or bronze muzzle-loaders—cannon royal, demi-cannon, culverins and culverin-bastards. The smallest guns, which were no larger than the modern ship's saluting gun, were invariably pointed towards the waist of the ship, as a warning to unruly crews to behave.

Two bronze cannon, cast in 1535 and 1628 respectively, were recently recovered from the wreck of an old Swedish warship, and were found to be only slightly corroded. The alloys used for these guns contained 84 per cent and 91 per cent of copper respectively with up to 14 per cent of tin and a little lead.

Dover Castle still possesses an ancient bronze cannon of $4\frac{3}{4}$ in. bore and 23 ft long, which is familiarly known as 'Queen Elizabeth's Pocket Pistol', while few visitors to Edinburgh Castle fail to notice Mons Meg (Fig. 18), which is 450 years old and was part of the defences of the Tower of London for 150 years.

5. Brass Wire

The woollen industry, on which much of England's prosperity depended prior to the Industrial Revolution, was one of the principal users of brass wire through the need for wool cards.

Carding is perhaps the most important process in woollen production. It has not changed essentially, except by the use of machines, for at least seven centuries. After being sorted, scoured, dried and teased, the fluffy masses of wool must be worked up into the yarn from which cloth is woven. This is done in two ways, depending on the length of the original fibres. Long-staple wools are combed to produce roughly parallel fibres which can then be worked into yarn. Short-staple wool, on the other hand, must be first prepared to make the fibres strong by interlacing them. For many centuries this operation was carried out by hand, the wool being worked between pairs of wool cards shaped rather like large butter-pats. Each card had one face covered with leather and thickly studded with short iron and brass wires, on which the material could be pulled in every direction. Carding machines did not come into use until 1748 and were not employed on a large scale until Arkwright's time a generation later.

One of the main activities of the Mineral and Battery Company of Shakespeare's day was to produce brass wire. The company had a monopoly that occasioned much outcry both in Parliament and in the country, and although the monopoly was eventually broken it was not before large quantities of brass wire had been smuggled in from the Continent.

Up to the Elizabethan period, copper or brass wire was drawn by hand in Britain by a very primitive process. One method consisted of two men seated on swings facing one another with a narrow strip of brass fastened to a belt round each man's waist. By propelling the swings with their feet they could swing apart and gradually produce a crude type of wire by stretching the brass.[15] Wire was also made by the equally laborious process of hammering, until that was superseded by drawing; this latter process is believed to have been invented at Nuremberg in the 14th Century. At first, drawn wire was pulled through a die by hand, but later by machinery driven by water- or horse-power.

6. The Pin Trade

Pins were an important end-product of brass wire and considerable numbers were also imported. At the accession of James I in 1603 strong petitions and protests by native pin-makers were continually laid before the Court and Parliament; and it was stated that no fewer than 20,000 people, including women and children, were engaged in this one trade. The process of manufacture again was hardly a speedy one. In 1543, during Henry VIII's reign, the sale of pins was prohibited by law unless they were 'double-headed and have the heads soldered fast to the shank'.[16] This particular law, however, was soon repealed.

7. Stained Glass Windows

In addition to their use in coloured glass, certain copper compounds play an important part in the production of stained glass, a craft in which the English, Germans, Italians and French of mediaeval times excelled. Despite the ravages of war, some magnificent examples of stained glasswork still survive in the cathedrals of Western Europe. The process differs from the manufacture of coloured glass in which pigments are introduced in the original melt; in stained glass the picture is painted on the glass surface. For this purpose a vitreous paste is employed, copper being one of the important constituents. The product is then heated so that the design and the glass fuse into one. It is a highly skilled and very delicate art, and it seems impossible to get quite the same effect by modern methods, because only age can bring out the brilliance of the colours at their very best.

From glass to windows is a simple transition and it is interesting to note that even Homer mentions a bronze window frame. With stained glass windows, the leading of the panels was held in place by copper wire.

8. Tudor Weights and Measures

Although weights and measures have always been preserved with great care, hardly any British weights survive that are older than the time of Henry VII. A very rare set of standard English wool weights, mostly 7 lb weight and dating from 1491, is still in existence. These are bronze, shield-shaped, and have holes at the top for slinging across the saddle-bow; the face bears the royal arms, in addition to other arms and marks.

The standard English measure of capacity was the Saxon bushel. One of King Edgar's is still preserved at Winchester, whence the common names Winchester Quart and Winchester Bushel have been handed down. These were reauthorized by Edward III, who was a great law-maker, in 1352. There also exist numerous fine old Winchester bushels, cast in bell metal, including one from Henry VIII's reign. These measures comprised the Elizabethan standards for a bushel, quart, gallon and pint, and were in service until 1824. A set of standard measures was kept in all the sixty chief towns in the kingdom. There is also in existence a set of Elizabethan avoirdupois weights, comprising 7, 14, 28 and 112 lb; they are of bronze and were cast in bell form. The standard of length was the same as that of the old ell, 36 inches.

Very stringent laws applied to false weights. For instance, the Letter-books of the City of London record whole series of bad deliveries on that score, for the unscrupulous tradesman was as ready to cheat then as at any time since. In those days, coal was sold in 8-bushel sacks, although it was often found that they contained only six. Offenders were tried before the Sheriff and they usually confessed. They were then ordered to stand in the pillory while their sacks were burnt under them; and in addition the coal was forfeited 'for the use of the Sheriffs'.[17]

The famous Elizabethan merchant trader and traveller Anthony Jenkinson, who with his pack-mules wandered over much of Russia and south-west Asia, took with him a 1 lb and a 1 oz brass weight to measure his drugs and other small things when among those semi-savage races.[18]

9. The Great Mediaeval Bronze Doors

On the Continent there are many striking and splendid reminders of the permanence of copper and bronze in the fine arts, especially from the

Renaissance period onwards. Italy is full of examples, embracing the whole of the 15th and 16th Centuries, when the native genius for art, under the protection of the powerful Dukes, the City States, and particularly the Papacy, flourished then as it has never done before or since. Of particular note are the many fine architectural remains which include a considerable number of magnificent sculptured bronze doors. In some cases their design can be traced back to the Imperial days of the Pantheon which possesses the oldest surviving bronze doors in the world. These were erected by Hadrian in A.D. 164, and are truly gigantic, being 39 ft high and 19 ft wide overall. They hang upon fluted bronze pilasters; and above them, in the ceiling of the portico, is an ancient bronze grating, just as it was erected 1800 years ago. On either side of this grand doorway stood colossal bronze statues of Augustus and Agrippa.

Similar designs were adopted in many of the larger Italian churches throughout the succeeding centuries. Florence has a number of examples, including some of the most famous of all, the three pairs of doors in the Baptistry. The South Door, which was designed by Andrea Pisano, was erected in 1336; its twenty-eight compartments show in relief events in the life of St. John the Baptist. The North Door, which also has twenty-eight panels, was mainly executed by Ghiberti between 1403 and 1424; while the celebrated East Door, the work of the same sculptor and only completed in his extreme old age, has rich reliefs of biblical subjects (Fig. 17). It was erected in 1452.

Rome also possesses some magnificent mediaeval bronze doors, Those of the Lateran Basilica, which was originally built by Constantine the Great, were taken from the Senate House. They were adapted for their new position by fitting a strip of bronze to each edge; but in all other respects they are reported to be unchanged. The three bronze doors in the main entrance to St. Peter's at Rome, which are embellished with a curious admixture of biblical and political subjects, were cast by A. Filarete and S. Ghini in 1445. Great new doors of bronze are now being made for St. Peter's at Rome.

There are in the north of Italy 9th Century bronze doors in the famous Basilica of Saint Ambrogio at Milan, and others may be seen in Pisa Cathedral (A.D. 1180), the Cathedral of Aix-la-Chapelle (A.D. 804); and several pairs still exist in the Basilica of St. Mark and the Baptistry at Venice. One of the latter, which was damascened in silver, is the oldest of its type in Europe. The Sacristy of the even more famous Basilica Ostiensis at Rome has silvered bronze doors which were cast by Staurakios at Constantinople in A.D. 1070; they contain fifty-four panels illustrating scenes from the New Testament.

10. Grilles, Gates, Tombs and Statues

The superb gates of Henry VII's Chapel at Westminster are of a different character from the massive bronze doors produced by the Italian craftsmen. Gilbert Scott, who examined them closely, reported that 'they were made of very small pieces of brass, copper and bronze, subsequently gilded. The junction of the pieces was so managed that it is difficult at first sight not to believe that the whole was cast in one piece'.[19] Within this Chapel, a very beautiful bronze grille surrounds the monarch's tomb.

The attractive colour of copper and the architectural alloys bronze and brass, their resistance to corrosion and capacity for taking a high polish, have ensured their universal use in church furniture through the centuries, right down to the modern Roman Catholic Cathedral at Westminster. Apart from grilles and altar rails, many old pyxes, monstrances, chalices, reliquaries, croziers, etc., still exist. These were frequently covered with beautiful ornamental work usually of almost pure copper, since this material was more ductile and easier to gild and enamel than bronze.

Among the very many lovely old tombs, which are either mainly or wholly of bronze, that of Mary of Burgundy at Bruges (1495) is a particularly fine example. The fine bronze figures on Henry VII's tomb at Westminster, and also those on the tomb of Margaret of Richmond in the same Chapel, were executed by no less a person than Torrigiano, the same who, when a student, quarrelled with his fellow-student Michael Angelo, and struck him such a blow on the nose as to disfigure the great sculptor for the rest of his life.

With regard to the more minor features of church buildings, architects have often exercised their fancy in designing bronze, copper and iron door-knockers. Some knockers in existence today are many hundreds of years old, and may have been used by fugitives from the law to claim sanctuary. One of these old knockers from Durham Cathedral is shown in Fig. 21.

Bronze was also used extensively for statuary although it took second place to marble. The famous bronzes of the period range from the great and noble statue of Gattemelata outside Padova Cathedral to quite small pieces, which were equally exquisite in their proportions. One of the most famous bronzes in the world is the Perseus at Florence, the work of Cellini. In this, as in much of his other work, Cellini was a complete master of the *cire perdue* method, and the same process was undoubtedly employed by his contemporaries. Few details are available regarding the techniques used by Renaissance craftsmen as the artists were always very secretive and each carefully concealed his own method of procedure.

17. One of the famous pairs of bronze doors of the Baptistry at Florence. These doors, which depict biblical subjects in relief, were the work of **Lorenzo Ghiberti** and were completed in 1453.

18. (*Above*) Visitors to Edinburgh Castle rarely fail to notice Mons Meg, the massive bronze cannon which was cast in the 16th Century and once formed part of the defences of the Tower of London.

19. (*Left*) Monumental brasses were a feature of many Church tombs in Britain and on the Continent from the Middle Ages onwards and although many have been melted down, about 10,000 still remain in Church floors all over England.

20. (*Top*) Many ingenious lock designs were produced in brass by master locksmiths in England from the 12th Century onwards. This detector lock not only had a secret catch to conceal the keyhole but could also record the number of times the door had been opened.

21. (*Left*) A bronze 'sanctuary' knocker on one of the doors of Durham Cathedral. Knockers of this type were used by fugitives in mediaeval times to claim the protection of the Church.

22. Brass and other copper alloys have been used in watch manufacture ever since the first rather cumbersome watches were produced in Germany during the 15th and 16th Centuries. This example from South Germany, made during the 18th Century, is nearly 6 in. in diameter.

23. (*Top, right*) Before the invention of the sextant, the brass astrolabe was essential for navigation. It was probably introduced into Europe by the Arabs and could be used to ascertain the latitude, the points of the compass, the time and even the heights of mountains.

24. An ornamental German clock dating from the mid-17th Century. The case is gilt copper and the dials are silver.

25. A coffee pot and a pair of candlesticks in English Sheffield plate, about 1760. This form of plating, in which copper was solid-plated with silver, was used extensively until the invention of electro-plating in the 19th Century.

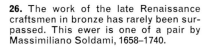

26. The work of the late Renaissance craftsmen in bronze has rarely been surpassed. This ewer is one of a pair by Massimiliano Soldami, 1658–1740.

27. A set of 17th Century French bronze cup weights and ornamental case. Modern weights, particularly the smaller sizes, are frequently brass.

28. (*Below*) When the wool trade was one of England's main sources of wealth, special bronze wool weights were provided, usually bearing the monarch's coat of arms or, as in this case, those of the Commonwealth.

29. Tudor plumbing—a ¾-in. bronze stopcock which was first installed at Hampton Court Palace in 1539.

A brass cistern, Ger-
man late 15th Century. An
early example of the use of
brass in a domestic water
system.

31. Celestial globe and stand—
Persian 1649. The globe is engraved brass with the constella-
tions inlaid in silver.

32. (*Below*) Bronze was a favourite
medium of the Renaissance sulp-
tors for works large and small.
This example, which depicts Hercules wrestling with a lion, is
Italian Florentine work. It dates
from about A.D. 1500 and is 7¾ in.
high.

Out of the multitude of bronze sculptures, two are worth special mention. In the year 1508, Michael Angelo, then a young man who had recently amazed the world by his unique colossal statue of David in marble, made a second large David, this time in bronze. The other example is a collection of bronze statues at the very lavish tomb at Innsbruck of the Emperor Maximilian. The statues represent heroes and also ancestors of the Emperor, and were executed partly by Peter Fischer early in the 16th Century, one of the most celebrated metal craftsmen of that age. Perhaps the finest work in the collection is his statue of King Arthur, despite the fact that the Celtic hero is clad in mediaeval armour.

11. Weather-Vanes

Weathercocks or vanes are of great antiquity. Although its natural place is at the summit of a tower or a church steeple, it is less clear why the traditional form of this old sign should be a cock. One authority has explained it as having a religious origin because 'the cock, like the preacher, watches throughout the night, marks the hours with his call, wakes the sleeper and celebrates the dawn'. Although copper is the traditional material for this purpose, the oldest known weathercock is of bronze. It stands above the summit of Brescia Cathedral, where it was fixed nearly eleven and a half centuries ago.

The coppersmiths who made old weather-vanes displayed both ingenuity and humour, hence the vast number of curious designs. Grasshoppers, the sign of Sir Thomas Gresham, founder of London's Royal Exchange, are common; so are ships. Above the relics of St. Michael's, a Wren church at Queenhithe, there is a three-masted barque vane which has successfully resisted the sooty atmosphere of the metropolis for nearly three hundred years. Flying foxes are also a favourite subject for weather-vanes. One neat symbol is a maltster's shovel vane which ornaments a brewery. Sonning Church has for its vane the figure of a parson preaching to empty chairs. Griffins, dragons, fishes, a blacksmith shoeing a horse, and to mention one with a modern note, a railway locomotive at Crewe, are other subjects of original design. On Standish Steeple, near Wigan, the crest of the Standish Family was utilized for the vane; it shows an owl seizing a rat.

12. Enamelling

Decorative enamelling, one of the oldest and mostly highly appreciated arts in the world, affords yet another use of copper. Specimens of exquisite workmanship, which still retain the brilliant colours of the enamels despite the wear and tear of the centuries, may be seen in museums and collections everywhere—some examples are almost priceless.

Art enamelling is usually applied to plates of a pure metal. Copper is the most favoured material but much beautiful work has also been achieved with gold and silver and to a lesser extent with bronze.

There are three principal enamelling techniques. First, champlevé, in which parts of the surface of the plate are cut away to leave a solid raised pattern. The hollows are then filled in with colours, and the article is afterwards cleaned, smoothed and baked. Next, there is cloisonné. In this case thin strips of metal are soldered edge-on to the object in order to produce the pattern, the spaces between being then filled in, and the whole baked as above. In the third class are the painted enamels, a branch for which Limoges was famous for hundreds of years, particularly during the 15th and 16th Centuries. This fine art has been revived during our own time, two of its greatest exponents being Alexander Fisher and Sir Hubert Herkomer. Painted enamels are usually copies of pictures, applied to flat or slightly curved surfaces such as a shallow dish; and the base is invariably a copper plate. The article is first coated all over with a continuous layer of plain enamel, on which the design is added by successive layers of colour. A splendid collection of old Limoges ware may be seen in the Victoria and Albert Museum, in London.

13. China and Japan in the Middle Ages

At a time when much of the Western world was in decline, copper and bronze craftwork flourished on a grand scale throughout the Orient in India, China and Japan.

The enormous pyramidal masses of the Central and South Indian temples with their superabundant sculptures were mainly worked in stone; but they also contain many fine bronzes including Buddhas large and small. Some of the immense Buddhas and bells that can be found in India, China and Japan must have occasioned the founders many a headache; but once successfully cast, they have endured to this day (Fig. 11).

There is also an Indian Temple of Ananda, at Tirumalai, which is unique in foreshadowing modern trends. It is entirely sheathed in copper sheet with elaborate hand-wrought ornamentation, an interesting parallel to the use of copper wall sheathing on a number of modern buildings.

14. Copper in the Pre-Columbian Civilizations of America

Archaeological excavations carried out in recent years show that although the Pre-Columbian cultures of Mexico, Central America and Peru were primarily 'stone-age', the various peoples—the Aztecs, Toltecs, Zapotecs, the Mayas and the Incas—possessed a fairly advanced knowledge of metalworking. In Mexico, where the Aztecs became the dominant power around the beginning of the 14th Century A.D., copper, tin and gold were worked as well as an alloy of copper and gold known as tumbaga.

The techniques of smelting, casting, beating, soldering and gilding were understood and most of the output of the metalworkers, who were organized in separate guilds, appears to have been in the form of ornaments. Some utilitarian objects have survived and those in copper include fish-hooks, needles, pincers, mirror frames, small picks, chisels and axes. All the peoples of Mesoamerica possessed great skill as stone-masons and it is fairly probable that they used copper tubes with water and abrasives to drill blocks of stone. Prescott reported that the Inca masons of Peru used stone, copper and bronze tools. The latter were reserved for the more difficult tasks, and modern analysis has shown that the bronze used consisted of 94 per cent copper and 6 per cent tin. With the abundant supplies of both metals in this part of the world it is hardly surprising that the use of this alloy developed there.

One group of objects, which have been found in sites all over Mexico and Central America, are ornamental clapperless copper bells. These were in the form of a hollow shell with a pebble enclosed through a vertical slit to make a noise. They were decorated with geometric designs and were usually one or two inches long but several specimens up to six inches in length have been found.

The more primitive North-American Indians also used copper for tools, weapons, ornaments and amulets. The copper was probably native copper which was abundant around the shores of Lake Superior, and with the general increase in archaeological excavations in recent years, a number of valuable examples have been discovered—mainly in burial mounds. Some of the objects unearthed are believed to be about 5,000 years old (Fig. 9) and are attributed to the 'Old Copper Culture' which existed in the Great Lakes Region at that time.

15. Early Bronze Casting in West Africa

Bronze casting, mainly by the *cire perdue* process, first developed into an art in West Africa during the period corresponding to the Middle Ages in European history. At a time when West Africa had only the slenderest links with the outside world, mainly through Arab slave-traders, the peoples of Benin and Ife and other regions in what is today modern

Nigeria began to produce beautiful bronzes, some of which still rank with the masterpieces of world sculpture.

Knowledge of the development of this separate African culture is far from complete but some of the earliest objects excavated so far date from the 12th and 13th Centuries, while others, notably those attributed to the Benin Kingdom, appear to have been cast between the 15th and 17th Centuries. A tomb recently excavated at Igbo in Eastern Nigeria contained a hoard of bronze objects including a number of highly decorated bowls and vases, pendants, amulets and ornaments which had been buried with the priest-king as part of his ritual regalia. Also recovered at the same site were examples of pottery, specimens of textiles and pieces of calabash. In this respect it is worth noting that the preservation of these organic materials is almost certainly due to the presence of copper in the bronzes which inhibited the action of white ants and bacteria. The most highly valued examples of West African bronze work are undoubtedly the cast heads, one of which is shown in Fig. 13. These have an almost classical style and show a mastery of technique which has rarely been surpassed.

5. The Industrial Revolution

1. Its Effect on Copper Mining

The Industrial Revolution brought about a tremendous change in the production of copper and its alloys. In the first place, an insistent demand arose for more and better raw material. In 1586 Ulrich Fosse, a German who was working the Cumberland copper mines, boasted that he could smelt 560 tons of copper ore in forty weeks. The 17th and 18th Centuries saw a vast improvement in this rate of output, largely arising from a quicker removal of impurities from the ore. By 1717 the Landore Works at Swansea comprised three large buildings, one of which was devoted solely to calcining. There were also thirty smelting furnaces for copper, lead and silver, a refining house, a test house and other outbuildings.[20]

In 1794 the Mines Royal at Neath Abbey were smelting 230 tons of copper ore per week to give 18 tons of copper. They used thirty-eight furnaces which consumed 315 tons of coal in the operation. The presence of good coal, in fact, was one of the reasons why the Swansea district became the centre of this industry; charcoal had been used right down to 1688 although as early as 1632 Edward Jorden discovered a new method of smelting by using pit coal, peat and turf as a fuel, and four years later Sir Philip Vernatt was granted a patent for the use of coal alone for that purpose.

Swansea was also an excellent seaport and was accessible to ships from all parts of the world which could bring ore from mines abroad.

During the 18th Century production in the nearby Cornish mines increased and a high output was sustained due to the introduction of steam pumps to remove the water from the diggings. This was the first use of steam power in mining and arose from the inventive mind of Thomas Newcomen, a Dartmouth blacksmith. Thus the Swansea district with its coal and commanding position became the greatest centre in the world of copper smelting and refining, a distinction which it retained until the latter part of the 19th Century. But a terrible price was paid; the local atmosphere in what had formerly been the beautiful green valleys became so foul with sulphurous fumes that it was said that if the Devil were to pass that way he would think he was going home.[21]

The cost of copper, in those days, was very great. In 1714 cake copper, unrefined, fetched £100 per ton, and plates as they came from the battery works cost £140 to £150 per ton. In 1694 Swedish copper, which was then regarded as high quality, cost £168 per ton. These figures, currency for currency, far exceed modern prices. On the other hand, the entire English output of English copper at that date was only about 100 tons per annum.

2. The Welsh Process

The Welsh Process of extracting and refining copper was long, costly and tedious when compared with modern techniques, but it remained more or less unchallenged until the mid-19th Century. In 1851, the year of the Great Exhibition, considerable improvements in the smelters were announced; but it was not until Bessemer's invention of the blast furnace, together with the employment of large reverberatory furnaces, that output improved. According to Alexander, the ore at Swansea, after being broken into small lumps by hammers, was hand-sorted by girls; hence much good metal must have been wasted. The selected ore was then calcined no fewer than three times to reduce the sulphur content down to about 11 per cent. The calcine was then smelted with suitable fluxes, the aim being to produce a *matte*, i.e. a molten mixture of copper and iron sulphides, which was cast into pigs. These were slowly reheated until they yielded blister copper which was about 98.5 per cent pure. Blister copper is so named because its upper surface is full of blowholes or blisters due to entrapped oxygen. To expel this oxygen the cake was remelted; and branches or poles of green wood were thrust into the molten metal. Combustion of the green wood occurred and this reduced the oxygen content to a mere trifle. This important stage was called 'poling'. Finally the metal was cast into billets and cakes suitable for wrought work. This product is known as tough pitch copper. It is a remarkable fact that despite all the modern metallurgical improvements, no better way has yet been found to deoxidize blister copper than the old-fashioned and picturesque one of poling.

3. Growth of the Brass Trades

Brass and tin bronze remained for centuries the principal copper alloys and it was not until the rapid development of metallurgy in the 19th Century that other and now familiar alloys began to be used. Brass long continued to be made from copper and calamine. Its production was not easy, particularly as the copper itself was not very pure; and small impurities in the pure metal and the alloy can have detrimental effects on both metals. It was only in 1738 that a patent was taken out by William Champion to distil metallic zinc (or spelter) from calamine, by reduction with charcoal or stone coal. The works at Bristol then began to produce a brass of high quality at the rate of 200 tons per annum. At that period both brass and copper were cast into billets and cakes in stone moulds and a particular virtue was attached to stone from St. Malo for that purpose.

Meanwhile the use of rolling mills was beginning to supplant the old battery mills for many products; but it was not until the mid-19th Century that really powerful rolling mills were installed, although the Dockwra mill at Swansea had been working since 1697.

4. Some More About Pins

The Dockwra Works specialized in the manufacture of brass pins. Their brass was 'passed between stones in order to beat out a plate of about 70 lb weight. This was cut into seven or eight strips, then stretched on the rolling mill operated by water power to the designed thinness and periodically annealed. The resulting sheets were then cut into many long threads and drawn into wire of the required sizes. The wire was cut into lengths of 5 or 6 yards and then into 6-inch or 8-inch pieces. The end was pointed on a machine and the wire cut off to the length of the pin; heading was done by stamping. The pins were then tinned and packed. Each of these operations was performed by a different workman and it was said that the best workmen could deal with 24,000 pins a day.'[22]

Other firms sold the long strips of wire for working up elsewhere.

The pin-making trades were centred mainly in the Birmingham district, along with brass founding for the manufacture of thimbles and similar items; others were near London, at Islington and Highgate.

Towards the end of the 18th Century, as more complex designs developed, the pumps employed in the mines and elsewhere required a steadily increasing number and variety of steam valves, safety valves, cocks, taps, flanges and similar parts, mainly in brass. By about 1770 all these things were being manufactured in the Midlands, besides grease-cups, gauges, whistles, pump cylinders, candlesticks and brassware generally.

5. Invention of the Stamping Press

An important invention, which speeded up the production of many brass articles and thereby increased this demand, was the stamping press. This was mainly due to John Pickering, a London toymaker, and Richard Ford and John Smith, both of Birmingham. In 1769 the first-named patented his machine for stamping articles out of sheet metal. It was a simple transition for Ford to employ shaped dies which enabled pots, pans, dishes and an unending variety of other things to be manufactured from sheets in bulk quantities. The stamps or presses had two steel dies, upper and lower, one being convex and the other concave, so that by impact or pressure the sheet could be cupped and formed according to the pattern of the dies. As a result of this development metal buttons became much more readily available; and many of the brass furniture fittings used by the master cabinet-makers of the period were made by stamping although some still had to be cast.

The invention of coining presses inevitably followed the development of the ordinary stamping press.

6. The Great Inventor-Craftsmen

Many of the improvements in metal-working techniques were due to the determination and persistence of men who were themselves skilled metal-workers. Newcomen was a blacksmith by trade, and Watt, who with the aid of his shrewd patron and partner Matthew Boulton finally constructed more efficient steam engines, was a trained instrument maker. At a later date the two Stephensons, father and son, were likewise within the same category. This combination of practical skill allied with an appreciation of the theoretical problems involved was responsible for the basic advances in technology, which precipitated the Industrial Revolution. The existence of skilled instrument makers and mechanics who were in the vanguard of these new developments can be attributed partly to various learned bodies of the day, particularly the Royal Society founded in 1660. Under its first secretary, Robert Hooke, the 'Royal' established a tradition for the performing of practical experiments which frequently required the services of a skilled artisan. As time passed the total of men who specialized in the construction of models and machines increased and their numbers were enlarged by a steady influx of refugee metalworkers from the Continent who sought asylum in this country. Notwithstanding this increased demand for its services, instrument making must have been a somewhat uncertain profession even in the middle of the 18th Century, and it appears to have been confined to certain localities. When James Watt was seeking instruction in how to manipulate brass and to learn the instrument trade generally, he had to come to London from Greenock in order to get employment. Even on returning to the Clyde, he would have fared badly had he not found employment at Glasgow University.

7. Josiah Wedgwood

The Industrial Revolution embraced almost every aspect of production; there were indeed few crafts that remained unaffected by this upsurge in industrial activity. The pottery industry was one among many that was revitalized and many of the changes that ensued can be attributed to Josiah Wedgwood, who opened his first china works in 1759. Wedgwood, in addition to adopting many beautiful classical and other designs, made a special study of glazes and was already known for his fine green-glazed ware. This was made to his own formula and included one-twelfth part of calcined copper. The standard formula for green glazes on pottery at that time was 'six pounds of sulphate of copper dissolved and precipitated by borax, then mixed with ten quarts of white glaze'.[23]

8. Bolsover and Sheffield Plate

In 1742 Thomas Bolsover, a Sheffield workman, was repairing a knife handle made of silver and copper when, by accidentally overheating it, he caused the metals to flow so that the silver formed a coating over the copper. He realized the commercial value of this discovery and exploited it to make small objects which, though looking like silver, were largely composed of the cheaper metal. Later, Joseph Hancock found that by making both plates separately, giving them the highest possible finish, fluxing and then heating them together under pressure they could be made to adhere. Usually the flux, which had been applied to the edges, covered the joint effectively; but in 1784 George Cadman adopted the practice of soldering on solid silver edging to ensure that the copper core was completely hidden. Thus was established yet another copper industry, Sheffield Plate. After a time of great prosperity its popularity fell away, and eventually it was largely superseded by the invention of electroplating during the 19th Century. However, it has come into favour again and many fine articles of Sheffield Plate may still be seen.

9. Navigational Instruments

In the construction of instruments for use at sea or in any moist, salt-laden atmosphere, brass has long been the first material of choice. This is due not only to its resistance to corrosion but also to its good machinability, to the ease with which scales and other marks can be engraved upon it, and perhaps most important of all, to its non-magnetic properties. It is because of the last-named reason that marine compasses are mounted upon brass binnacles, equipped with brass compass bowls, and swung in brass gimbals. The elaborately fashioned navigational instruments of sailing-ship days, as far back as the 16th Century, were often magnificently engraved, as is well shown by the superb astrolabe in Fig. 23. An instrument of this type was used by Columbus, but astrolabes were known very much earlier. The instrument resulted from a combination of the Pre-Christian armilla and the theodolite; and was well known in the Near East, whence it was introduced into Europe by the Arabs, perhaps about A.D. 700. Astrolabes were generally made of brass. They ranged from a couple of inches in diameter up to a foot or more; and a very fine collection may be seen in the National Maritime Museum at Greenwich. With the aid of an astrolabe, one could ascertain the latitude, the points of the compass, the time, the heights of mountains, and even, if one believed in astrology, one's horoscope.

10. Brass Clocks and Watches

Another industry for which brass was found to have special advantages was the manufacture of clocks and subsequently watches. It is not known who made the earliest true clocks, but they extend back at least to the 10th or 11th Centuries. Their working mechanism was then extremely primitive with gear wheels either carved out of hardwood or made of wrought iron. Some of the earliest known true clocks were installed in Old St. Paul's (1286), in Canterbury Cathedral (1292) and in Exeter Cathedral (1300).

Clocks derive their name from the French *cloche*, doubtless because they included a bell which sounded the hours. Clocks with a striking mechanism appear to have been introduced in the 14th Century. There exists a very remarkable old astronomical clock by Giovanni Dondi, which, in addition to telling the time, shows correctly all the movements of the planets; it was made entirely of brass and copper. Time, itself, was apparently not of much consequence in those days, for Dondi took sixteen years to complete this masterpiece, from 1348 to 1364.

Early bracket or chamber clocks were almost invariably encased in gilt bronze or brass. The working parts were generally also of brass; and as glass was not used for clock faces until the 16th Century the dial was normally engraved on a brass face. A brass clock, made in 1632, was stated recently to be still in its original condition and keeping good time. Clocks have always exercised a fascination and many wonderful examples of the art may be seen in museums all over the world. Both the Wallace Collection and the Victoria and Albert Museum in London possess a number of priceless exhibits. Those in the Wallace Collection are mostly of the 17th and 18th Centuries and the majority are still kept working. The collection at the Victoria and Albert Museum is devoted mainly to watches and is perhaps the finest in Europe, but it also includes a number of remarkable old clocks (Figs. 22 and 24). The ornamentation on all these old clocks is lavish and in fact the great majority of the intricate chamber, bracket, lantern and other clocks that were produced up to the 19th Century had brass faces often engraved and chased.

The earliest known watches were made at Nuremberg at the end of the 15th Century. They were large and ungainly; some, in fact, resembled an egg so much that they were called 'Nuremberg eggs'. Refinement in design gradually transformed them into the flatter and more practical form of later times.

One major improvement lay in the escapement, the first effective one being invented by Thomas Tompion (1639–1713). Graham, Le Roy, Earnshaw and Harrison were among the celebrated watchmakers who followed him. John Harrison (1693–1776), in particular, earned great fame by making his famous chronometer, and thereby winning an Admiralty prize of £20,000 in 1761. The immense value of the reward was due to the long-standing need for accurately ascertaining the time at sea, in order to determine the ship's longitude.

Harrison, who had begun as a Yorkshire carpenter's son, made a clock with wooden wheels while still a boy. He persevered with practical clock-making, and like others attempted to solve the longitude problem; his success came when he thought of the idea of an accurate compensation-curb which would alter the effective length of the balance spring in proportion to the expansion or contraction caused by changes in temperature. His invention was given a very severe test. It was wound up and sent to Jamaica and back; on its return after several months, it was found to have lost only 1 minute 54½ seconds. Harrison, like the other master clock-makers, worked in brass.

11. Copper Engraving Plates

A very important use of copper, from the Middle Ages down to our own day, has been for engraving plates, both for etchings and the printing of maps. This art even antedated the invention of printing by movable types. The great artist Albrecht Dürer, who was perhaps the finest etcher of all time, worked very largely on copper plates; as did Rembrandt and countless others who have followed these illustrious examples. Other materials have been tried, but none has ever seriously challenged the pre-eminence of copper for this purpose. Steel engravings, for instance, were very popular in mid-Victorian days and gave very fine results; but a steel plate will rust if not stored carefully and is also harder to engrave. The copper used for engraving is alloyed with a very small addition of silver or arsenic to raise its annealing temperature slightly when heated.

Copper plates for the production of pictures and other illustrations date from at least A.D. 1430 in Germany, where they were employed to produce playing cards. 'The Passion of Christ' was engraved on a small copper plate in 1440 and, before this date, the engraved letters on the leather and parchment covers of manuscript books were made by letters in relief in brass stamps.

Copper plates were also adopted centuries ago as the best means of engraving maps. The first maps known to have been printed from copper plates were two Italian editions of the geographer Ptolemy, in 1472. Metal supplanted wood for this purpose because of the clarity and much finer detail that could be reproduced on the polished copper surface. There still exists an engraved copper globe of about 1493 which was made just after Columbus's first voyage to America.

Both in H.M. Ordnance Survey maps and in Admiralty charts the use of copper plates for map printing is traditional. These maps and charts require constant correction whenever new roads are cut or new soundings show different depths of water. Such corrections are easily made on a copper plate. The official practice has been to scrape or gouge out the old details, and then to carefully hammer back the portion of the plate in order to make the surface perfectly level once more, before inscribing the new features on it. Many of the Admiralty plates have been subjected to this procedure repeatedly for more than a century and still remain in use.

12. Architecture and the Fine Arts

During the 18th and 19th Centuries copper and bronze continued to hold a prominent position in the fine arts which has been maintained down to the present day. Bronze became a favourite medium for sculpture and thousands of fine bronzes of the period are still in existence all over the world. Hamo Thorneycroft's work and the bronzes of Rodin and Epstein, as well as bronzes such as those in Coventry Cathedral, are more modern examples of this art.

When Wren was commissioned to rebuild St. Paul's Cathedral after the Great Fire of London he intended to use copper for the dome. This would have lessened very considerably its enormous weight; but there were no coppersmiths capable of undertaking the work, and the specification was altered in favour of lead. An old copper roof covers the Chapel Royal, St. James's, but the majority of the handsome green copper roofs and cupolas in Britain were erected in the 19th Century or even more recently (see p. 79). On the Continent many of the oldest and most attractive copper roofs are to be found at Copenhagen. These include the roof of the Danish Parliament building and the City Hall, as well as other examples dating back over 350 years.

13. Development of the Copper Coinage

Although the most celebrated copper alloy coin—the brass farthing—never existed, both the pure and alloyed metal have, with silver coins, formed the basis of the British coinage. Queen Elizabeth would never agree to a copper currency, but she did allow copper token money towards the end of her reign. It fell into disfavour, however, and James I prohibited tokens altogether. In 1613 he gave authority to Lord Harington to issue some more or less experimental copper farthings; but the first real British copper currency dates from 1672, when a halfpenny and a farthing were minted. These were made of pure Swedish copper, with 175 grs. to the halfpenny and $87\frac{1}{2}$ grs. to the farthing. All these coins were produced by the old-fashioned method of hammering which was not supplanted until after the invention of the stamping press a century later. The Isle of Man had its own copper currency in the Stuart period, with farthings and half-pence bearing the island's three-legged symbol. It continued to issue its own money until 1864.

Throughout the ages governments have, on the whole, honestly sought to maintain the value of the coinage except when debasement was deemed part of the royal prerogative. A constant struggle has been waged against counterfeiters who found a ready means of illegal profit both by clipping and by substituting base metal. During the middle of the 18th Century the tremendous increase in counterfeiting in England created a scandal. The Birmingham district was the centre of this malpractice, notably in respect of copper; very severe penalties were exacted and dead counterfeiters were constantly seen to be swinging from the gibbets on Handsworth Heath.

Matthew Boulton—the partner and supporter of James Watt—was one of the men responsible for the further development of a copper coinage. Boulton was, in fact, one of the first 'industrialists'. He acquired a large interest in the copper and tin mines, and, as he was a staunch believer in an honest currency, he devoted much thought and skill to perfecting a coining press. Copper money was by that time almost out of circulation, and so great was the shortage that various manufacturers were allowed to issue token money (Fig. 33). By means of a special collar applied to the dies, Boulton succeeded in producing coins of a standard size and weight which exactly fitted a tubular gauge; this enabled spurious money to be detected instantly by its weight alone. He then started to manufacture for abroad coins of such excellence that the Government promised him a contract to mint pennies; but the Royal Mint succeeded, by passive resistance, in delaying the order for ten years, until 1797. Meanwhile, Boulton continued to mint copper in large quantities, including his token money, the famous Boulton penny. At one date he even outran the supply of raw copper. His description of his own mint at Soho, Birmingham, in 1792 is interesting:

> 'This mint consists of eight large coining machines, which are sufficiently strong to coin the largest money in current use, or even medals; and each machine is capable of being adjusted in a few minutes so as to strike any number of pieces from 50 to 120 per minute. Each piece being struck in a steel collar, the whole number are perfectly round and of equal diameter.'[24]

Boulton's presses could manufacture as much as 1,200 tons of coins a year. His first official contract for the British Government was for two-penny pieces, pennies, halfpennies and farthings. It amounted to 4,200 tons between 1797 and 1806.

An interesting footnote concerning the Boulton penny relates to the practice of adding these coins to molten iron when 'specially good metal was required'. This foreshadowed modern metallurgical developments, in which controlled amounts of copper are added to cast iron to improve strength, corrosion resistance and machinability. Boulton also issued some very fine medals in bronze and the precious metals, employing in their design only artists of the highest calibre such as Flaxman.

14. The Old Horse-Brasses

An interesting little sideline in the history of brass, which has a special relation to the 18th Century, is the manufacture of horse-brasses. These were either made of lead covered with brass or from hand-hammered and cut brass; some of the older ones were also in precious metals. Horse-brasses occur in great variety: over 1,200 different designs are known. The basis of the design is usually a ring or circle within which stars, half-moons, camels, birds, unicorns and many other figures are enclosed. The origin of horse-brasses is extremely old; according to the specialist collector, Mr. H. S. Richards, bronze horse 'brasses' were made two thousand years ago. They were originally amulets and were intended to ward off sickness or accident. Now they repose proudly in cabinets; a few appear at horse-shows, but most of these specimens are modern.

15. Copper and Brass in Ships

The use of copper for sheathing the bottoms of wooden ships was first introduced in the middle of the 18th Century. The oak timbers of the old wooden sailing-ships were always liable to be attacked by the dreaded teredo or shipworm when in warm seas. This is not really a worm but a boring mollusc which can work its way into quite hard wood by means of sharp teeth at the end of the shell. Once inside, the pest goes whither it will, usually with the grain, and deposits its eggs in the hole which it has bored. Quite stout timbers, including the piles used for fronting wharves, become so riddled with the shipworm's tunnels as to be rotten beyond repair. Copper sheathing was tried as a remedy by the Admiralty, who had the frigate *Alarm* sheathed with copper in 1761. This not only protected the ship but also improved her speed by keeping her bottom freer from barnacles and other marine organisms. The experiment was so successful that within a few years most of the Fleet, including the flagship *Victory*, were given copper bottoms; and the practice was naturally extended to the large East Indiamen and other vessels sailing in tropical waters.

Copper was used exclusively until 1832. In that year G. F. Muntz patented a new brass containing 60 per cent copper and 40 per cent zinc which is known either as Muntz metal or 'yellow metal' in the trade. As it was much cheaper and almost as effective, it inevitably supplanted copper for sheathing and was also widely used on wharves. The advent of iron ships fifteen to twenty years later altered the position, but Muntz metal sheets continued to be used in smaller vessels for this purpose. The Admiralty now specifies approximately the same mixture of copper and zinc, with an addition of about 1 per cent of tin; this is known as 'naval brass'. During the Second World War nearly all Admiralty motor fishing vessels and other small craft operating in warm harbours and seas were sheathed in Muntz metal on a base of tarred felt.

Another notable feature of the warships of Nelson's day was the resurrection of brass cannon. Some ships were equipped with large brass carronades, a terrible weapon which, by contemporary accounts, was feared much more than the conventional cast iron guns because of its far greater accuracy and range.

6. Copper in Electrical Engineering

1. Dawn of a New Science

When the great Elizabethan experimenter William Gilbert, after many years' work, published his book *De Magnete*, and first defined scientifically a number of fundamental ideas about magnetism and electricity, he started a chain of operations that eventually led to the vast, dynamic and complex electrical engineering industry of today which consumes two million tons of copper annually. It was Gilbert incidentally who coined the word 'Electrica' from the Greek word *elektron*, meaning amber, a substance which featured in his experiments.

Electrical engineering in the industrial sense is only about a hundred years old and followed from Faraday's epoch-making discovery of electro-magnetic induction in 1831; its roots, however, extend back much earlier, even before Volta's famous 'pile' of 1800, when the relative values of metals as conductors of electricity were well known. The success achieved by using copper in these classic experiments led to its general use in this field long before the theoretical reasons were understood. Hence all the early experimenters soon found themselves using copper sheets and wires whilst brass, because of its non-magnetic properties and ease of working, was specified for structural parts.

A notable milestone in early electrical research was the invention of the Leyden Jar in 1745. Two years later Sir William Watson, who was deeply interested in electrical phenomena, succeeded in transmitting a current 2410 feet across Westminster Bridge, using the River Thames as the return circuit. He also noticed that the effect was apparently instantaneous. Stephen Gray had already found that some bodies conducted electricity well, whereas others did not, the first conception of dielectrics; and in 1729 he used brass wire for the first known attempt to transmit an electric current. Thus began a series of experiments by a number of investigators to determine which were the best transmitters of the 'electric fluid', as it was

33. Macclesfield Copper Works truck token issued in 1790. Truck money was paid on the understanding that it should be spent in the employer's shops or stores and, like the official coins of the realm, truck tokens were invariably copper.

34. (*Below*) Herschel's polishing machine and brass mount used in polishing speculum. The latter is a copper-tin alloy of white silvery appearance which was formerly used almost exclusively for mirrors and reflectors.

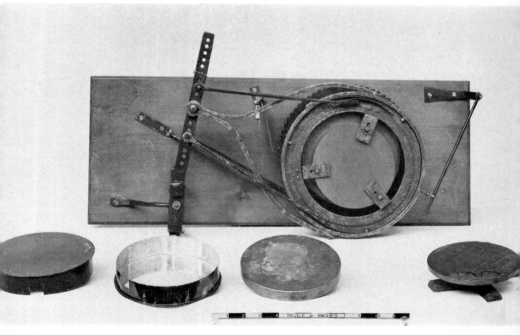

35. Faraday's Induction Coil—the first electrical transformer and one of the most treasured possessions of the Royal Institution. It consists of a soft iron ring around which were wound five coils of copper wire.

36. (*Below*) A short length of the first British commercial telegraph which was laid by Cooke and Wheatstone in 1837. It linked Euston Station and Camden Town, and consisted of five copper wires supported in grooved wooden blocks.

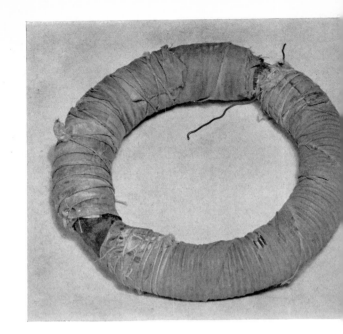

37. Brass, which has always been a popular material for electrical instrument parts, was used extensively by Samuel Morse for his early transmitting keys. This is a replica of equipment for his second telegraph constructed in 1846.

38. (*Below*) Laying the first submarine cable constructed from copper conductor wires from Dover to Cap Grisnez, 1850.

39. (*Above*) The Atlantic cable of 1865—searching for a fault after recovery of the cable. It was for this application that 'high conductivity copper' was first produced.

40. (*Left*) The Henley galvanometer used for receiving the first signals through the Atlantic Cable in August 1858.

41. Wilde's multipolar dynamo of 1866–7 required over 500 lb of copper strip and wire. A modern 500 MW a.c. generator contains about 14 tons of copper for the windings and other components.

42. The world's first 3-phase a.c. turbo-generator built in 1900 to supply power to a colliery at Featherstone, Yorkshire. Apart from the use of copper for the generator windings, the lubricating oil and cooling water pipes, drain cocks etc. were in copper or copper alloys.

43. Another famous first—Marconi's copper induction coil and tuning inductance from his first radio transmitter constructed in 1899.

44. Thirty years' rapid progress have already made the original Watson-Watt radar receiver of 1935 look slightly antedeluvian. Copper, as today, was used exclusively for wiring circuits.

45. Inserting the copper windings in the stator of a modern 500 MW a.c. turbo-generator. The copper conductors are water-cooled and each weighs over 250 lb.

46. (*Below*) In recent years the introduction of the copper printed circuit has revolutionized wiring in the electrical and electronics industries.

47. (*Above*) The modernizatio[n] British Railways, involving electrification of lines form[erly] served by steam, has led to [the] erection of thousands of ton[s] copper and cadmium copper o[ver]head conductors.

48. Copper in modern under[sea] communications. Wiring of [the] submerged repeater unit is c[ar]ried out in air-conditioned are[a] with the operators wearing spe[cial] clothing to avoid contaminatio[n] called: it was soon proved that metals were the most successful and that of these, copper, even in its relatively impure state, was superior to all others except silver.

2. *Franklin's Lightning Conductor*

It was while living in Philadelphia that Benjamin Franklin, the 18th Century statesman and natural philosopher, became convinced that electricity and lightning were the same phenomenon. The Leyden Jar made it practicable to prove this supposition and in 1752 he began his celebrated experiments with kites. He succeeded in flying an ordinary silk kite on a light wooden cross during a thunderstorm. The centre of the cross was provided with a sharp iron spike and below was a key which was in contact with a Leyden Jar. To his delight the lightning caused a flow of current which was clearly indicated by the jar. After many such experiments, Franklin concluded that buildings might be protected against lightning in the same way by a pointed wire standing erect above the roof with the lower end buried in the ground.

In 1769 Franklin visited England and lightning-conductors to his specification were erected on St. Paul's Cathedral. These conductors were of iron, 4 in. $\times \frac{1}{2}$ in. in section. Their electrical resistance was so high that when the Cathedral was struck by lightning in 1772, portions of one conductor were made red-hot by the passage of the discharge.

As a consequence copper came to be used for lightning conductors, an application for which it has been virtually unchallenged ever since. In 1811 copper wire was employed to protect ships' masts; prior to this it had been customary for vessels to carry copper chains which had to be hoisted to the masthead whenever a storm appeared to be imminent; contact with the sea was made by means of a connexion outside the hull. Hoisting the chains was not always carried out sufficiently rapidly, so that the ship was often damaged before they could be got into position. It was therefore decided to fix permanent conductors, and at the suggestion of Benjamin Cook copper strips were run down each of the masts and through the hull to the ship's bottom which, in the case of naval vessels, was usually sheathed in the same metal. Through sheer ignorance, the remedy was sometimes almost as bad as the cause, for it is recorded that on one man-o'-war the conductor actually passed through the powder magazine.[25]

3. *Cavendish*

Henry Cavendish (1731–1810) made the first measurements of electrical capacity, and he also determined very exactly the electrical conductivity of a number of different substances. Cavendish was an eccentric recluse who made little attempt to publish his findings and most of his work had to be rediscovered forty or fifty years afterwards, with result that others received the credit. An example of this was his discovery of the fundamental law of electrical flow in 1781 which had to be subsequently rediscovered by Ohm forty-six years later. He also enumerated all the laws of the division of electric currents between circuits in parallel (1776); and he determined the law according to which electric force varies as the distance. Sir Ambrose Fleming, in a masterly summary of electrical history,[26] justly describes Cavendish as the Kelvin of the 18th Century.

4. The Voltaic Pile and its Consequences

The next great step forward can be attributed to Alessandro Volta, who in 1799, following close upon the discovery of the galvanic effect by Galvani, built the first electric battery. This immediately became known as Volta's Pile and, like many other batteries which followed it, employed copper as an active element. It actually comprised discs of copper and zinc placed one upon the other, with a layer of wet cloth between each pair. The adoption of wet cloth as a separator was a fortunate afterthought, for although Volta himself believed that the current flow arose from the contact of the metals and not from any chemical action, the part played by an electrolyte in the action of a cell had yet to be discovered. This phenomenon in fact started a controversy which lasted throughout the 19th Century, with giants such as Kelvin supporting Volta's point and Michael Faraday favouring the chemical view.

The potentialities of this new source of energy were quickly realized and battery design was soon improved by Cruickshank, also by the many-sided Wollaston and Sir Humphrey Davy. In 1809 John Children constructed a battery having twenty pairs of copper and zinc plates, each plate being 6 ft long and 2 ft 8 in. wide; thus it involved 320 sq. ft of copper and had a total cell capacity of 945 gallons. John Children used this huge apparatus in further experiments to determine which was the best electrical conductor. In the same year Davy aimed still higher. He was the Professor at the new Royal Institution and he succeeded in inducing his patrons to provide funds for building a battery that had 2,000 pairs of copper and zinc plates, with a total surface area of 890 sq. ft. The first experiment with this great battery enabled him to produce an electric arc between carbon electrodes.

Among the most important applications which followed the construction of these large batteries was the electric telegraph. This was a landmark in the development of communications and also created a tremendous demand for copper wire.

5. *The Widening Field*

In 1820 Oersted discovered the connexion between the polarity of the Voltaic pile and that of the magnet, and he also proved the existence of a magnetic field. In 1821 Michael Faraday discovered electro-magnetic rotation by causing a wire conveying a voltaic current to rotate continuously round the pole of a permanent magnet. W. Sturgeon in 1824 wound a copper wire round a horseshoe-shaped iron bar and showed that the bar was powerfully magnetized when the voltaic current was passed through the wire: this was the discovery of the electro-magnet. Soon similar electro-magnets of great power were being built, both by Sturgeon himself and, in the United States, by Joseph Henry, as well as by Faraday and others. An immediate consequence of this development was the invention of the galvanometer.

Arago showed that a copper plate rotating under a suspended magnetic needle tended to drag the needle after it and *vice versa*. Finally, Ampère found that a magnet could be made to rotate on its own axis when a current was passed through it. Various other scientists then showed that a copper disc could be made to rotate between the poles of a horseshoe magnet, when a current was passed through the disc from the centre to the circumference. This was the first electric motor.

All these factors led Faraday to his clear conception that there existed 'lines of magnetic force'.

6. *Faraday's Famous Ten Days*

What would happen if one cut the lines of magnetic force?

Armed with a practical knowledge of all that had yet been achieved in electro-magnetism, Faraday began, in August 1831, ten days of intensive work at the Royal Institution which had a revolutionary effect. Ever since 1825 he had been querying whether an electric current passing through a conductor could not induce an electric current in a neighbouring conductor. On 29 August 1831 he succeeded in doing this with a 6 in. diameter iron ring, round which were wound five coils of copper wire, three on one side of the ring and two on the other. One of these coils was connected to the voltaic pile and the other to a galvanometer. The moment that the current in the battery was started, a transitory current appeared in the galvanometer in the opposite direction.

This was the famous Induction Coil (Fig. 35). The apparatus, which is now one of the treasured possessions of the Institution, was the first electrical transformer ever made. Modern transformers, some of which have capacities of up to 550 MVA and contain well over 40 tons of copper, are still constructed on the same principle.

Faraday then proceeded to prove that the lines of magnetic force could be cut, and a current induced, by simply rotating a copper disc by hand between the poles of a powerful electro-magnet. This second fundamental discovery is the principle of the dynamo; it was soon applied in practice in the form of a number of small power-driven electric generators although a good many years elapsed, and numerous improvements had to be made, before they became very efficient. In 1841 power-driven multipolar machines were employed in Birmingham for the electroplating of copper articles and by 1858 a generator for electric light had been installed in the North Foreland Lighthouse.

7. The Development of the Dynamo

The size of dynamos or electrical generators grew rapidly. Faraday's original apparatus involved only about $7\frac{1}{4}$ lb of copper but the armature of a machine built by H. Wilde in 1866 required 576 lb of copper strip and wire (Fig. 41). This machine, which was belt-driven, was described at the time as 'a machine of enormous and unprecedented power', with an output 'so enormous as to melt 15 inches of No. 11 copper wire'. By comparison, a modern 500 MW turbo-generator operates at several hundred times the voltage of Wilde's machine and requires about 14 tons of copper for various components in the machine.

Contributions to the general development of the dynamo were made by Field, Edison, Sprague and others; whilst a particularly important advance in armature winding was made by Z. T. Gramme, who in 1870 invented (or rather reinvented, following Pacinotti in 1860) the toothed-ring winding system for armatures. His armature consisted of a ring of iron wound over with an endless coil of wire and connected to a commutator consisting of copper bars insulated from each other. Gramme dynamos were then soon made on the self-exciting principle. In 1873 it was discovered at Vienna that a dynamo of the Gramme type could also act as an electric motor and one was set in rotation when a current was passed into it from a similar machine. 'Henceforth the electric transmission of power came within the possibilities of engineering.'[27]

The brothers Siemens exhibited an electric tramcar in Paris in 1881. By using transformers, L. Gaulard in 1883 proposed to employ high-pressure alternating currents for the distribution of electricity over wider areas. Polyphase alternators and the long-distance transmission of electrical power by polyphase electrical currents were both first exhibited at the Frankfurt Exhibition in 1891.

In addition to those scientists already named, outstanding men in the 'heroic age' of electrical engineering included J. Hopkinson, Crompton, S. P. Thompson, Mordey and Ferranti, with the combined theoretical and practical genius of Kelvin behind them all.

These developments led to a tremendous increase in the supply of electric power; but demand, as today, soon threatened to outstrip supply. The introduction of power distribution systems for electricity supply, the installation of land and submarine telegraph cables, and the use of electric traction for trains were among the major consequences of the rapid progress in electrical engineering during the latter half of the 19th Century.

8. The Electric Telegraph

The first recorded uses of electric cables were for exploding mines and for telegraphy. The mines were exploded in the Baltic by the Russian Schilling in 1812, and the first telegraphed messages were transmitted by Francis Ronalds in 1816 through a copper wire laid underground. Insulated cables date from 1838, the original insulating materials being tarred rubber and pitch-covered yarn.

Beginning with work by Ampère in 1820, various sytems of telegraphy were invented and tried out before Cooke and Wheatstone installed the first British electric telegraph to be put into commercial use in 1837; this was on a stretch of the London and North-Western Railway between Euston and Chalk Farm (Fig. 36). In 1843 a similar installation was put into service between Paddington Station and Slough, on the Great Western Railway. These systems employed copper conductors and required five wires supported in grooved wooden blocks. Almost simultaneously Henry and Morse were undertaking similar projects in the United States.

In 1846 the first British commercial telegraph company was formed, and after twenty years had elapsed, three of these companies owned between them no less than 16,000 miles of line.

9. The First Submarine Cables

Immediately the telegraph was established successfully on land attempts were made to adapt it for submarine working. In 1845 Jacob and Watkins Brett laid a single copper wire covered with gutta-percha between England

and France. This cable, which was unprotected, unfortunately broke after only one day's operation, but the feasibility of the project had been proved. A year later an armoured cable was laid at the same spot; this cable had four separately insulated solid conductors which proved to be entirely satisfactory. It was followed by T. R. Crampton with a permanent line from Dover to Calais (1851).

10. The Atlantic Cable

There ensued the much more ambitious project of laying a cable across the floor of the Atlantic Ocean which involved sinking the cable to the sea-bed four miles or more below the surface, together with the difficulties of landing at both ends, on Valentia Island and Nova Scotia respectively. In 1856 a company was formed with a capital of £350,000 and the great enterprise, which called for no less than 17,500 miles of 22 s.w.g. copper wire, began.

Apart from the mechanical difficulties of splicing and laying such a long cable, those concerned had to take one vital decision at the outset: it was a decision based on the very sparse information available at the time and unfortunately it was a wrong one.

Electrical messages suffer a slight amount of 'friction' in transmission so that what would be an instantaneous signal over a short distance becomes a long-drawn-out wave at the receiving end of a very long length of wire; how much greater, then, must this retardation of the electrical impulse be at a point two thousand miles away! On the other hand, the slower the message the less possible would it be either to identify the signal or to work the cable at a profit.

Kelvin, who was then Professor William Thomson, had already discerned this weakness of cables and had published some important notes on the subject, wherein he showed that the retardation, which is proportional to the length, depended also upon the capacity of the wire and of its gutta-percha covering. He therefore recommended a thick wire for this cable and a heavy covering, coupled with the use of only the most minute currents. This in turn involved the construction of a very accurate detector, for which purpose he subsequently invented the delicately balanced mirror galvanometer mentioned below. When at last the Atlantic cable project took shape he was appointed one of the eighteen directors, but without any particular duties or powers.

Whitehouse, in charge of the scheme, was a man of considerable ability but fixed ideas whose views were entirely opposite to Thomson's. Sir Charles Bright was the Chief Engineer. Whitehouse advocated a small cable and the use of a high current to overcome its resistance, and this procedure was adopted.

By July 1857 the cable was ready. It comprised 1200 pieces of copper wire each two miles long. Before being shipped they were joined into lengths of 300 miles; one half was carried by the U.S. frigate *Niagara* and the remainder by H.M.S. *Agamemnon*. Thomson sailed in an unofficial capacity on the *Agamemnon*, Whitehouse remaining ashore at the Irish end. The expedition commenced work from Valentia Island on 5 August, but after 400 miles had been successfully laid the cable broke and the ships returned home for the winter.

The experience gained during this voyage convinced Thomson that Whitehouse was wrong, but he had not sufficient power to enforce his views upon the Board. In the succeeding winter he invented his mirror galvanometer which was designed to detect even the faintest currents. It comprised a small mirror affixed to a tiny magnet; the mirror reflected the light from a lamp on to a scale that was graduated in degrees. The slightest trace of current made the magnet move together with the attached mirror, thereby causing a spot of light to travel along the scale. Despite its delicacy, this exquisite instrument could be used effectively even during a storm.

Thomson was also perplexed by the unexpected difficulty that had been found in getting currents to pass through copper. He had a number of samples analysed and it was then found that they were not equally pure, although of very high grade (between 98.76 per cent and 99.2 per cent). He raised this question with the other Directors who did not think it of much consequence, and with the manufacturers, who said that it was commercially impossible to make the quality of copper that he required. Nevertheless the Professor stuck to his ground, with the result that the makers *did* achieve what had been considered impossible. Thus was born 'high conductivity copper', which every electrical engineer now specifies as a matter of course.

On 10 June 1858 the two ships sailed again, Thomson now being in charge of the electrical testing room on the *Agamemnon*. His 'stethoscope', the mirror galvanometer, went with him. After many misadventures—including a terrible storm in which the cable broke loose in the hold and was damaged, and the testing room was flooded with salt-water—the ships succeeded in landing both ends on the same day (5 August). The galvanometer rendered invaluable service throughout, its tiny spot of light being observed 'as anxiously as a physician watches a patient during a crisis'. The first message ever sent from Europe to America by wire flashed under the sea, a response was received, and as the cable seemed in perfect order it was handed over to Whitehouse. Great was the jubilation both in London and in New York. The directors of the enterprise became public heroes, Thomson in particular receiving a civic welcome on his return to Glasgow.

The rejoicings, however, proved to be premature. Messages steadily became more and more difficult to transmit, until finally, on 28 August, the cable failed completely. An investigation showed that Whitehouse, despite Thomson's warnings, had been using his powerful current on a cable that was already damaged by the storm at sea. A violent quarrel broke out between the electrical engineer and the directors, the shareholders lost their capital, and for some time the name of the Transatlantic Cable was not a safe one to use in City circles. However, Thomson, Bright and a few other leading men never lost faith in the ultimate practicability of the enterprise. After a discreet interval the project was revived, a new company found the necessary money, and a fresh cable was made and thoroughly tested. On this occasion Thomson's advice was followed, the conductor being made three times as thick as its predecessor with the current reduced to a minimum. The *Great Eastern*, the famous old paddle-steamer and largest ship of its day, was specially adapted to carry it, and in July 1865 she started westwards. After 1200 miles had been laid the cable broke, its end falling to the sea-floor two and a half miles below. The ship was laid across the line of her outward course and the cable was found again, but unfortunately her apparatus for grappling with it was not sufficiently strong. Once more the expedition had to return home but this time all on board were confident that success must eventually be theirs. A new cable was manufactured. Just a year later it was laid quietly and uneventfully. Furthermore, the broken end of the other cable was recovered, quite undamaged; the joint was spliced and this second line run on to Newfoundland.

The heroes of this great achievement, including Thomson, were honoured by knighthoods.[28]

11. Electricity Generation and Supply

Since those exciting early days there has been a tremendous increase in the size and complexity of copper cables, and new and more efficient means of laying, recovering and repairing cables at sea have been developed. Today every continent is linked by a number of lines, some of very intricate construction. On land, in the industrial countries of the world there is everywhere a vast network of both underground and overhead lines, for communications and for the distribution of power; some of these require a number of different materials and a very high degree of protection, usually by serving and sheathing. There are also countless miles of insulated copper wire in use for the distribution of electricity to houses, flats and commercial and industrial buildings.

Copper conductor cables range from the simple insulated pair of wires, which operates a door-bell, up to multi-core cables which may comprise hundreds of separate copper wires. One of the largest standard power cable cores contains 169 copper wires, each 0.107 in. in diameter.

The manufacture of a modern power cable, whether high or low voltage, is extremely complex and involves numerous operations—stranding, insulating, sheathing, armouring. In general, the required number of copper wires is first stranded and then insulated with a covering of paper, rubber, varnished cambric, cotton or plastics. The cores are then twisted together with a suitable lay, the interstices being packed with a filler so as to give the whole an approximately circular cross-section. Sometimes the cable is next given a stout outer sheath of lead or aluminium; and in circumstances where there is a possibility of mechanical damage, the cable may also be armoured with steel armour wires. Certain long cables are also oil- or gas-filled for use at high voltages.*

Modern telephone cables are even more complex and may comprise no fewer than 18 'units', each unit having 101 pairs of copper wires, or 1818 pairs of wires in all.

One way of satisfying the increasing demand for electricity has been by increasing the voltage. In 1890 the first high-voltage underground mains in this country were installed by Ferranti between Deptford and London. Four mains, each about seven miles long, were laid and put into service at 10,000 volts. The conductors in each main consisted of two concentric copper tubes insulated with resin-impregnated paper, the diameter of the inner tube being about 0.8 in. and that of the outer one 1.9 in. This project involved nearly 140 tons of copper alone.

A year later, in 1891, the first demonstration of long-distance three-phase high-voltage transmission by means of an overhead line was made in Germany, at the Frankfurt Electrical Exhibition. This installation, which was the forerunner of our present-day high-voltage transmission systems, employed three copper wires supported on porcelain insulators and wooden poles. The line, which was 110 miles long, was used to transmit power from generators at Lauffen on the Neckar to Frankfurt, where it was harnessed to light the Exhibition and to work the exhibits.

The transmission of electricity supply led to the need for central power stations, a fact which was realized very early by both Edison and Lane Fox. In 1881 Edison established in Pearl Street, New York, the first public

* See C.D.A. Publication No. 56, *Copper Cables*.

electric supply station. A year later another was opened in England, in the basement of a house in Holborn Viaduct, London. Edison, whose inventiveness was proverbial, designed electric meters, electric mains, lamp fittings and generators complete for the purpose. By 1882 numerous electric lighting supply companies had been formed; but in Britain a misguided Act of Parliament hindered their progress until 1888, when the Act was amended.

12. Cadmium Copper

One of the features of copper metallurgy is that copper can be easily alloyed with other metals. The addition of about 1 per cent of cadmium results in an alloy which has a considerably higher tensile strength than electrical grade copper although there is a slight reduction in conductivity.

Cadmium copper trolley wires were used almost exclusively for tram and trolleybus services, both in London and in the provinces for many years until these vehicles were replaced by buses. Cadmium copper was also used during the original construction of the National Grid between the Wars—notably for river crossings such as the one at Dagenham where seven cables were suspended across the Thames from towers 487 ft high. Today, this same alloy is being used extensively for catenary wires and contact wires in the overhead electrification systems of British Railways; and for railways abroad. It has been estimated that for every 100 miles of electrified track 2500 tons of copper and cadmium copper may be required.

13. The Telephone

In 1879 the first telephone exchanges were constructed in Britain and America, following the invention of the telephone by Alexander Graham Bell three years earlier.

Bell's dramatic story has often been told. He was a young Edinburgh man who was interested in deafness. He migrated to America for his health and became Professor of Vocal Physiology at Boston University in 1873. There he tried to reproduce sounds by the vibration of a plate. 'If I could make a current of electricity vary', he said, 'precisely as the air varies during the production of sound, I should be able to transmit speech telegraphically.' The 'miracle' was accomplished on 10 March 1876, when his assistant, who was in another room, heard him say, 'Mr. Watson, come here; I want you'. In the same year the new instrument was shown at the Philadelphia Exhibition. 'With my ear pressed against this disc', said the delighted judge who was examining the exhibits, 'I heard it speak distinctly several sentences.'

Modern telephone exchanges contain a large amount of expensive and complicated equipment. Apart from the obvious use of copper for telephone lines, vast numbers of spring contacts for telephone exchange equipment are made of nickel silver, a copper–nickel–zinc alloy with excellent wear and corrosion resistance.

14. Electric Lighting

The last quarter of the 19th Century witnessed notable advances in the development of electric lighting, the most important pioneers being Edison, Swan and Lane Fox. In 1879 Edison succeeded in making a successful lamp in an evacuated glass bulb; this contained a carbonized filament, into which the current was passed through fine platinum wires. It was first shown commercially in London in 1882. Many different types of lamps have followed this beginning, although lamps operating on Davy's carbon arc principle of nearly a century earlier were still used in London and elsewhere until well in the 20th Century. The passage of a current through neon, sodium and other gases, without a filament, is a comparatively modern development and now provides brilliant street lighting and illuminated signs, and is beginning to be used for household as well as office and factory lighting.

An important part of the ordinary electric bulb, the lamp-holder, is nearly always stamped out of brass. So suitable is this alloy for this purpose that when, owing to a temporary shortage of brass a few years ago, another material was used, the manufacturers reverted to brass as soon as possible, although the alternative was cheaper. Plastics have made considerable advances during recent years for non-conducting components. This has also been the case with small household switches; but brass contacts, screws and other parts are still of course essential.

15. Radio and Radar

Another great Victorian, Heinrich Hertz, lived only thirty-seven years (1857–94), but in his short creative career he was able to discover, by the most ingenious methods, a whole range of hitherto unimagined electric waves which could be reflected and refracted like waves of light. It was from the knowledge of the Hertzian waves that wireless telegraphy was developed by Marconi and others; and this has been followed during the past thirty years by the development of television and radar. Then began another enormous modern industry using vast amounts of copper and copper alloys for applications which now include printed circuits and wave-guides.

7. Copper in the Modern World

1. The Raw Material

At the beginning of the present century the world's annual demand for copper was about half a million tons; the United States produced about half of this total, whilst Britain's output had fallen to a mere token figure. Today the annual consumption is now more than nine times as large. This dramatic rise in the intervening sixty years can be attributed partly to population growth but mainly to the tremendous technological advances which have received impetus from two World Wars. In the Second World War the demand for copper most certainly could not have been satisfied, but for an invention in 1921, when Perkins patented his process of chemical flotation. This made it possible to mine ores which, up to that time, had been regarded almost everywhere as worthless. Some attempts at flotation of crushed ores had been made ever since 1860, but the process only became commercially important after the 1914–18 war.[29]

2. The Flotation Process

Until quite recently copper ore had to be hand-picked if the extraction of the metal was to be economical. In fact, in the last century, ores of 4 per cent grade were regarded as almost valueless. Today such ores (which would be regarded as relatively rich in copper) are scarce; the great majority of mines contain the metal in finely disseminated particles which aggregate anything from 2 per cent down to 1 per cent or even 0.8 per cent of copper. Thus to obtain metallic copper, up to 99 per cent of the material mined must be removed as waste. Only the flotation process mentioned above could make this practicable; and even so, it requires large companies with huge plant, continuous working and immense capital. This explains why, in order to smelt 4 million tons of new copper in 1963, nearly 400 million tons of ore had to be handled and treated in various ways.

Flotation depends on the fact that the grains of some minerals, and especially of metals, differ in the degree to which their surfaces can be wetted by a suitable solution. The powdered product of grinding the ore is fed into a series of tanks called flotation cells which are filled with a solution containing various oils capable of forming a froth. Air is pumped into each cell, the solution being agitated to bring a froth of bubbles to the surface. In the case of copper minerals, the particles adhere to this froth, which is separated, whereas the great bulk of the useless material sinks to the bottom of the tanks. By varying the chemical conditions within the cells different results can be obtained, thereby making flotation highly selective in skilled hands.

3. Smelting, Refining and their Products

The product of flotation is called 'concentrate'. It is passed on to the smelter and, after further processing, refining takes place, either on the spot or perhaps hundreds of miles away. Most refining is done in great batteries of electrolytic tanks. Some indication of the scale on which these operations are conducted is given by the great size of the reverberatory smelting furnaces and the impressive extent of some of the larger tank-houses. A large modern reverberatory may be a single chamber 130 ft long, 25 ft wide, and 12 ft high. This will smelt 1,000 tons per day of concentrate or calcine, and in some cases much more; and it does this continuously for over a year before it need be emptied and relined with refractory bricks. A typical tank-house contains a large number of concrete tanks, each carrying about thirty-six pairs of impure copper slabs which are the anodes, and thinner sheets of pure copper; it is on the faces of the latter that additional pure copper is deposited as the anodes are electrolytically decomposed. A large tank-house may contain 1,500 tanks, requiring perhaps 100,000 anodes and cathodes. All this represents a tremendous advance from the techniques used at Swansea only a hundred years ago!

The final products of smelting and electrolytic refining are cathodes, cast often in the form of copper wirebars and cakes.* The castings are subsequently worked in various ways into wrought forms. Re-melted cathodes may also be cast into ingot bars suitable for the preparation of alloys.

4. The Chief Copper Alloys

The industrial importance of copper in the 20th Century has been extended enormously by the ease with which it combines with other metals.

* See C.D.A. Publication No. 52, *Introduction to Copper*.

Tin and zinc are and always have been the principal alloying elements, but there are now many others—aluminium, beryllium, chromium, manganese, etc.—which form alloys with special mechanical and physical properties. Copper alloys now in fact play an indispensable part in everyday life even for such unspectacular items as shoe-eyelets, 'gold' powder compacts, 'silver' spoons and forks in daily use by the million, the 'gold' paint on cigarette packets, and for zip fasteners, costume jewellery and bird cages. These are but a few of the common things in which copper is a major constituent; in addition there are many even more unobtrusive uses of copper, e.g. in large cast iron engine liners, as a 'flash' in electroplating, and as moulds for plastics: even the little bunches of bristles in tooth- and nail-brushes are held firmly in place by tiny wedges of nickel silver which is a copper alloy.

The alloys containing copper fall into two main types: these are *copper-base alloys*, such as brass, tin bronze and aluminium bronze, in which copper itself is the predominant element; *and copper-bearing materials*, such as certain aluminium alloys, high-duty alloys to resist severe corrosion, and steels and cast irons which are improved by small additions of copper. The proprietary alloy 'Monel', a mixture of copper and nickel in which the nickel predominates, occupies an intermediate field between these two main classes.*

5. Copper in Modern Architecture, Building and Plumbing

Copper and its alloys are being used on an increasing scale in architecture and building. A large number of post-war houses have been roofed with copper, 2,000 on one site alone, and in thousands of dwellings all over Britain copper plumbing systems have been installed. One of the universal features of post-war domestic building has been the construction of large blocks of flats and offices, and here copper has made a notable contribution not only for ordinary plumbing but also for central heating and air-conditioning equipment, roofing, and even, as in Scandinavia, external cladding (Fig. 52).

There is also a demand for copper sheet and strip for dormers, gutters, flashing, canopies and cills; and copper and copper alloys are often used for glazing bars, fascias, frames, the grilles on bank counters, the nameplates on doors and various other forms of architectural metalwork.

One very special use in building, which is really associated with radio and radar transmission, is in sheathing, or more strictly shielding, so as to

* See C.D.A. Publication No.36, *Copper and Copper Alloys; Compositions and Mechanical Properties.*

ensure wave-free silence and cut out interference. This is one of the reasons for the considerable use of copper in the G.P.O. transmission tower which has just been erected in London. This spectacular addition to London's skyline, 620 ft high and at present the tallest building in Britain, also contains many miles of copper cabling and wiring to operate the telephone and telegraphic equipment, the lighting system and the mechanism to revolve the remarkable aerial restaurant situated 500 ft above ground.

Another notable and rather unusual building is the London Planetarium, erected in 1957, which is capped with an impressive dome sheathed in copper.

Other important buildings which also have copper roofs include the dome of the British Museum (one of the largest in existence), the dome of the Old Bailey, the roofs of the 20th Century cathedrals of Guildford, Liverpool and Coventry, the Festival Hall in London, and the Capitol building at Washington. The continuing use of copper in modern church architecture is demonstrated by its selection for the cathedrals mentioned above and this use extends beyond roofing to a variety of symbolic and decorative metalwork, such as the recently erected cross and orb surmounting Brompton Oratory which are bronze castings covered with gold foil.

Copper inevitably plays a vital part in the lighting, heating, air conditioning and sanitation of the giant skyscrapers of today. The recent Chase Manhatten Plaza, in New York, which is sixty stories high and the sixth tallest building in the world, employs about 60,000 ft of copper tubes for its plumbing services alone. Modern architecture, particularly the tower block type of building, has been criticized as monotonous, but architects are now beginning to specify wall panelling in copper or copper alloys; this not only protects the structure but gives a very pleasing effect. This practice was first adopted some time ago in Sweden, Denmark and Finland, and has since spread across the Atlantic, where the recent Seagram Building in New York is an outstanding example.

6. Shipbuilding

Many copper alloys were introduced largely because of their excellent resistance to corrosion by salt-water and salt-laden atmospheres; they have found also applications where a wear resistance greater than that possessed by pure copper is required. Thus aluminium bronze, manganese bronze, aluminium brass, gunmetal, cupro-nickel and 'Monel' are copper alloys which have long been standard materials for shipbuilding.

In the evolution of warship construction the battleship has been replaced by the aircraft carrier and vessels such as the *Vanguard,* the *King George V* and the American *Missouri* have gone for ever. Recently several new classes of warship have been introduced. These include small commando carriers and guided missile destroyers which are virtually small cruisers. Since the Second World War the optimum size of ocean-going liners on the North Atlantic route has declined slightly and vessels like the *Queen Elizabeth* and *Queen Mary* are no longer built. Nevertheless in all new construction, both naval and merchant marine, from 2 to 3 per cent of the deadweight is in copper and copper alloys.

Ships' propellers in small coastal vessels may be cast iron, but for warships and the vast majority of merchant vessels, copper alloys, such as high tensile brass or aluminium bronze, are invariably used. The propellers of a large ship may weigh up to 20 to 25 tons apiece (35 tons in the two *Queens*); and as spare propellers must be carried on board, this is in more than one sense a heavy item! The very heavy tailshafts of big ships are usually Admiralty gunmetal (a copper–tin–zinc alloy in proportions of 88/10/2), and the rudder stocks and massive propeller cone-nuts are often in the same material.

It is in the engine- and boiler-rooms of a ship where copper and copper alloys are used to the greatest extent. Marine condenser tubes are invariably 70/30 cupro-nickel or arsenical aluminium brass, two alloys which are particularly resistant to the severe corrosive and erosive effects of rapidly flowing sea-water. The world's first nuclear-powered merchant ship, *Savannah,* has more than 30 tons of cupro-nickel condenser tubes; while the main condensers of the modern liner *Empress of Britain* each comprise 5,949 cupro-nickel tubes, with tube-plates and baffles of naval brass, a copper–zinc–tin alloy (62/37/1). Undoubtedly the great new Cunarder, now on the drawing-board, will follow this practice. Copper and copper alloys are used for the feed-water, fresh-water and salt-water cooling systems, for ships' evaporators, low temperature steam lines and for numerous items of auxiliary equipment such as pumps, feed heaters, valves and miscellaneous coolers. Among the specific uses which have arisen in recent years is the use of aluminium brass pipes for the large heating coils of oil tankers. Some of these vessels are giants of up to 100,000 tons with dozens of oil-storage tanks, and the heating systems are on a corresponding scale.

The electrical equipment in a ship has grown extraordinarily complex and, as on land, the generators, electric motors, lighting and communications systems depend almost entirely upon copper and copper alloys for their operation. With the advent of wireless telegraphy before the first world war and radar during the second, a considerable amount of space is

49. An aerial view of the plant area of the Mufulira mine, Zambia—the Commonwealth's largest underground copper mine.

50. The Zambian mines in the famous Copperbelt are among the richest in the world. A large proportion of British copper comes from this source.

51. (*Above*) Copper sheet has been used for roofing many notable examples of modern British architecture. One of the most striking buildings recently erected in London—the Commonwealth Institute Building—has a roof of complex design fabricated from about 25 tons of 24 s.w.g. copper sheet.

52. (*Left*) Many Scandinavian architects make considerable use of copper for side-cladding of buildings—a typical example is this multi-storey block of flats in the Stockholm suburb of Kevinge.

53. Over 60 tons of 24 s.w.g. copper sheet were used for the roof of the Crystal Palace sports centre opened in 1964.

54. A modern police station in Finland faced with fluted copper infill panels.

55. (*Left*) Installing copper wiring cables in the hold of a freight-carrying aircraft. Other uses of copper and copper alloys in modern aircraft include the hydraulic service systems, brake assemblies and oil coolers for jet engines.

56. (*Below*) Copper alloys such as manganese bronze and aluminium bronze are used for large ships' propellers because of their excellent resistance to sea water corrosion and erosion.

57. (*Above*) Part of the water-cooled copper windings for NIMROD. About 300 tons of hollow copper extrusions were used for the circular electro-magnet for the proton synchroton at the Rutherford High Energy Laboratory.

58. (*Right*) Copper alloy Four-drinier wire, usually brass and phosphor bronze, plays an important part in modern papermaking mainly on account of its ability to resist the combined corrosive action of the wet paper pulp, water and the chemicals used in the process.

59. (*Above*) Whisky stills ar invariably made of copper. the pot-still process the ma whisky is distilled twice an two identical copper stills ar used as shown.

60. (*Left*) Copper in the mod ern car is mostly hidden be neath the surface but neve theless an average of abou 40-lb of copper and copper al loys is used in practical every vehicle built today Among the items featured i this composite illustration ar engine gaskets, radiators, th starting motor wiring an bright trim which has coppe plating beneath the chromium

61. (*Right*) Welding the internal seams of a 20-ton copper alloy chemical vessel. Recent advances in welding copper and copper alloys ensure that they can be used for modern methods of plnta fabrication.

62. (*Below*) The excellent ductility of copper makes it particularly suitable for modern heat exchangers for the chemical industry which are often an intricate assembly of interwoven copper tubing.

63. Solar energy in S.E. England—30 miles from London. The pool in this Sussex hotel can be maintained at a temperature of between 18–24°C (65–75°F) during the summer months by the solar heater shown on the right which consists essentially of about 7 cwt of copper tubing.

64. Mineral-insulated copper-sheathed cable being laid at the Aston underpass in Birmingham. Numerous other installations have been made in London and other parts of the country to prevent ice formation on road gradients during winter.

65. Five thousand years' experience dating back to the Ancient Egyptians is behind this modern copper prefabricated plumbing assembly. Copper is particularly suitable for the prefabricating techniques which are being increasingly employed to speed up building.

now given over to communications equipment, particularly in warships, where it is standard practice to duplicate vital equipment. This precaution is not only confined to naval ships; for example, the *Empress of Britain* has an emergency system of thirty-five strategic points, each of which can communicate back to the control room.

Naval ordnance has changed out of all recognition since the brass cannon of the 16th and 17th Centuries, but if the gun-barrels no longer contain copper they are fired electrically and considerable use of copper piping is made for the turret hydraulic systems.

The value of sheathing a ship's bottom in warm waters or polluted harbours has already been mentioned; but another trouble, to which all ships both steel and wood are liable, is the perpetual growth of fouling organisms, such as barnacles, ascidians, small tube-forming worms and weeds. This can be largely inhibited by covering the underwater parts with a composition that will poison the layers of sea-water immediately adjacent. Very many such anti-fouling paints have been tried, but only two have been found of much value, one including mercury and the other copper salts.

Small boat design and construction has made spectacular progress during the past twenty years. Rising standards of living have made it possible for many people to possess a boat of their own—in U.S.A. alone there are now nearly a million private motor-boats, yachts and other small craft. Copper alloys such as manganese bronze are used for centre-boards, rudders and propellers, and naval brass is used for propeller shafts and miscellaneous deck fittings. Wood is still strongly favoured for small boats and copper alloy wood screws and nails, generally silicon bronze, have long been recognized as the most suitable fasteners for all-wood construction. Many of the screws are now thread-rolled, a more economical process than screw-cutting since no swarf is formed.

Most of the uses of copper mentioned hitherto in this section have resulted from careful research and development based on experience over the centuries, but probably few specific items of equipment have been so effective or vitally significant as the de-gaussing apparatus which was hastily improvised during the early part of the last war. German magnetic mines were then sinking Allied and neutral shipping indiscriminately at an alarming rate. The mines were laid in shallow waters, even in the Thames Estuary, and detonated magnetically as soon as the ship's steel hull passed overhead. The resulting uprush of water usually broke the ship's back. Many ships were sunk and others, including the battleship *Nelson*, were damaged by this form of attack. Fortunately, the counter-measures devised were simple and completely effective. It was found that by attaching a copper strip around the hull and passing a current through it the ship's magnetic field was neutralized and the mines therefore failed to explode. All ships were subsequently provided with a de-gaussing system and by D-Day 1944 no fewer than 18,000 vessels had been protected in this way. On the large capital ships a considerable tonnage of copper was required—the *Vanguard*, which was completed immediately after the war, required twenty-eight miles of copper wire weighing 30 tons for the purpose.

7. The Railways and other Traction on Land

The passing of the steam engine from the railways of the world continues to evoke feelings of nostalgia among enthusiasts from nine to ninety but, although the replacement of steam by diesel traction is irrevocable, it has not meant an overall decline in the use of copper in locomotive and permanent-way construction.

On the contrary, the modernization of British Railways which is now in full swing is requiring very large amounts of copper and certain copper alloys, including about 10,000 tons of copper and cadmium copper conductors for the overhead electrification of the two main lines from London to the North (Fig. 47). There is also a considerable use of copper in signalling systems, besides all the miscellaneous needs for pantographs, switchgear, brake systems, motor windings, commutator bars, large and small service stations, etc.

The principal use of copper in the old steam locomotives was for the large firebox plates, although in certain later construction when the boiler generated superheated steam the use of copper was restricted because of the higher temperatures involved. Copper firebox plates have been used for locomotives ever since Stephenson's *Rocket* was built in 1829. The cylindrical boiler of the *Rocket* contained a firebox with a double copper wrapper-plate forming a water-jacketed top and sides, the front and back being dry plates; copper tubes connected the water and steam spaces of the firebox with those of the barrel. The heating surface of the Rocket's firebox was 20 sq. ft; by contrast, that of the *Royal Scot*, a famous engine designed by Sir Henry Fowler in 1927 for the London to Glasgow service, had a heating surface of 189 sq. ft. The notable old *Silver Link* (1935), which was used to pull the Silver Jubilee train between London and Newcastle, had an even larger copper firebox within which the whole of the *Rocket* could have been packed quite easily. The Stephensons chose copper for their fireboxes because of its successful use in large brewing and boiling vessels.

As far as motive power in the 20th Century is concerned the internal combustion engine is undoubtedly the power unit *par excellence*, as illustrated by its use in road vehicles ranging from motor-cycles and cars to tractors and heavy trucks. Although its coefficient of friction is not as low as some materials, copper was used for bearings of heavy tanks and other vehicles during the last war, and since then oil-filled, self-lubricating bearings and sintered copper materials have also been developed for i.c. engine use. Copper-lead bearings are also in demand because of their exceptionally high fatigue strength.

The average car, whether private or commercial, appears to contain little copper or copper-alloys but, in fact, has from 40 to 45 lb, according to type and size (Fig. 60). Gaskets are often of copper or an alloy such as 80/20 cupro-nickel which is recommended for high-duty engines. The most important application of copper in motor-cars, however, is in the radiator, where the heads and cores are generally copper with tubes of thin brass strip or foil, and the crimped fins of copper.

8. Money

When Britain and other countries went off the Gold Standard, they were quite unintentionally initiating a Copper Standard for coins of all values; this has proved to be particularly the case throughout the British Commonwealth.

The golden sovereign was never minted from pure gold, since this would have been too soft for such a purpose. Golden money was standardized in Great Britain at 22-carat, or in other words eleven-twelfths pure; the remainder comprised either silver or copper. Before World War One, silver money was about $99\frac{1}{4}$ per cent pure, the rest being copper; but the value of the richer metal increased, so that between the two world wars British silver coins never contained more than 50 per cent, a figure which for manufacturing reasons was varied slightly from time to time; the balance was copper. After 1945 the great rise in the price of silver made it necessary even to call in these coins, and in 1947 a cupro-nickel currency was introduced in which the percentages were 75 copper and 25 nickel.

Current 'copper' money contains 95.5 per cent copper, 3 per cent tin and 1.5 per cent zinc. (These and all such figures vary slightly from time to time, depending on the market value of each metal; this always has been the case with monetary currency everywhere.) The threepenny pieces are of brass, viz. copper 79 per cent, zinc 20 per cent, tin 1 per cent.

The total world production of copper coins absorbs thousands of tons of copper every year. The Royal Mint in London alone minted 700 million bronze and cupro-nickel coins in one recent year, representing nearly 7,000 tons of metal.

Coining presses are also used today to make vast numbers of badges, tokens and medals, on a scale which was hitherto unprecedented.

9. Paper Manufacture

If this were not the Electrical or Nuclear Age, it would certainly deserve to be remembered as the Paper Age, for never has so much paper been used or printed upon, by so many people or for so many purposes. Paper making is a fairly complex process and involves the use of machines which include a wide variety of rollers, wheels, semi-liquid pumps and wire gauze, all comprising a considerable proportion of copper alloys.

Good papers are made from rags, straw, grasses, etc., and newsprint from pulpwood trees. The principal method of making paper by machine is worth outlining. First, the raw material is 'digested' in vats, i.e. it is cleaned, bleached and softened in an acid solution. The digester is equipped with copper or brass cooling pipes, while the evaporation of the surplus liquor involves copper evaporator tubes and sometimes copper cylinders—applications where copper is chosen for its very high thermal conductivity. The bleached stock, a thick semi-fluid mass, is pumped into beaters, where the fibres are chopped up and shredded and the whole is reduced to an even consistency. This is the most important operation in paper making. The beater comprises a large revolving roll or cone, in stone, steel or bronze, into which are set numerous sharp-edged, flat-ended beater bars; these oppose similar bars set in a baseplate. A beater roll may be 5 ft in diameter, and weigh 10 tons or more with up to 160 bars. Normally the beater bars are made of 94/6 tin bronze; but aluminium bronze and other alloys are also used. On leaving the beater trough the paper material is an even pulp. It is pumped into feeding tanks, from which it is spread over the surface of a rapidly moving endless wire cloth screen, 40 to 60 mesh, or occasionally even finer. This screen, known as the Fourdrinier wire, is a weave of brass and phosphor bronze wire (Fig. 58). It is kept perfectly flat, although it may be more than 20 ft wide; and it runs on a series of small brass or copper rollers. In one giant machine, the screen is 26 ft 8 in. wide and 100 ft long. As the pulp passes along, surplus moisture is drawn out from below by suction, and the screen is vibrated so as to felt the small fibres together. Above the far end of the screen is a small, wire-covered hollow cylinder called a dandy-roll, which smooths the upper surface of the pulp and at the same time impresses a watermark into it if required. The product now resembles wet paper. It passes over a very large perforated suction roll, then between heavy pressing rolls, and next through smoothing rolls, the lower of which is usually made of bronze or gunmetal. Finally it traverses a vertical stack of rolls, commonly five in number, where it is calendered or given its surface finish. The paper is then wound into rolls.

Plunger, vacuum or centrifugal pumps are necessary to handle the fluid stock and these include a large number of copper alloy components, as do the vacuum boxes.

10. Printing

The use of photographs in book and magazine production has long since supplanted hand-engraving, for which a considerable amount of copper was used. Nevertheless the use of copper has increased. Today, by far the larger part of book illustration, except in the case of line blocks which are generally zinc, is by means of 'half-tone blocks' or their copies, 'electros'. These are produced by photo-engraving, which is also known as process engraving.

A half-tone printed picture is made up, as a magnifying glass will show, of thousands of dots of ink large and small, large dots in the lightest areas, grading down into fine dots in the shadows. A copper plate with the polished surface sensitized by an emulsion, usually bichromated fish glue, has the image of the photograph impressed upon it in a camera; and a glass screen, ruled to a suitable mesh, is inserted between the negative and the plate, so as to regulate the sizes of the dots and thereby the quality of the half-tone. The sensitized plate is then heated or 'burnt in' until the glue becomes a hard enamel. To avoid softening the copper on heating, process plates always contain a little silver or arsenic, which raises its softening temperature. The plate is now etched, so as to make the dots stand up in relief and thereby provide a printing surface.

One interesting application of copper in printing is in the making of matrices for 'Linotype' and other automatic type-setting machines. The compositor presses a keyboard on the machine, rather like a typewriter keyboard, and as each key is depressed a small piece of brass called a matrix is released from an inclined storage rack or magazine. The matrices are each impressed with a letter or figure; leaded brass is usually employed, although copper or bronze may also be used. A belt conveyor carries the released matrix to a box, where it joins others to form all the words in a line. The operator then presses a small lever which moves the line opposite the mould wheel, and the whole line is cast in one piece or slug by pumping in molten type-metal. After trimming, the finished slug is delivered on to the galley; meanwhile, the matrices are automatically returned to their magazines.

Another very interesting use for copper which has come to the fore during recent years is the printed circuit, now so widely employed by electrical engineers everywhere, especially in the electronics industry. This shows the value of applying the techniques established in one industry to another completely different in structure and outlook. Wherever elaborate wiring layouts are involved, as in radio and television sets, computers, etc., an immense amount of labour in wiring and fixing the circuits may be saved by simply photographing the wiring diagram on to a copper sheet, which can then be etched so as to leave the diagram in relief (Fig. 46). By punching holes through the points of connexion, through which terminal wires or tags from valves or other parts pass, and soldering these tags to the plate, the circuits are established; thus, by the aid of dip-soldering, all the joints can be fixed in a single operation. For the circuits themselves a laminated sheet is employed, having a face and sometimes also a base of copper foil which is bonded to a sheet of plastic.

11. Clocks and Watches Again

Modern clocks and watches are mass-produced on a very large scale. The material most commonly employed is known as 'clock brass'; a typical grade of clock brass usually contains 1.5 to 2 per cent of lead and about 59 per cent copper, the remainder being zinc. This alloy has long been the standard material for most of the working parts of clocks, timepieces, watches and instruments possessing a clock mechanism. The flat wheels are stamped out in vast numbers from strip of the appropriate thickness, while the supporting plates, though sometimes of steel, are also often of brass. Pinion wheels are made from long lengths of extruded brass rods of similar composition which are cut off in the small pieces required for each wheel. Brass or some other copper alloy is commonly employed for engraved clock faces, as well as for screws and fittings. A very large number of the cheaper types of watches have been made in gunmetal, while others are plated nickel silver.

Until the development of suitable machine tools all clock and watch parts had to be made by hand. An expert workman made the first or master clock, which was afterwards taken to pieces and the separate parts copied as exactly as possible by less highly skilled craftsmen. Prior to about 1850 six clocks per day were considered a large output for one manufacturer. The use of power-presses and very accurate dies has so altered the rate of production that a single clock-maker can now turn out from 10,000 to 30,000 clocks and watches in a single day, and at an infinitely cheaper cost. In a normal year from 10 to 12 million clocks and watches are produced in Great Britain alone.

The hands of some of the world's most famous clocks are made either of copper or a copper alloy. The hour hands of Big Ben at Westminster are solid gunmetal, and the minute hands, which are 14 ft long, are of tubular copper. The great clock hands on the Metropolitan Life Building tower in New York have iron frames sheathed in copper; the minute hands are 17 ft long and weigh 1,000 lb each, and the hour hands are 13 ft long and weigh 700 lb each.

12. General Engineering

Diversification is the keynote of the use of copper and copper alloys in current general engineering practice. With such a wide range of materials available in a variety of forms, such as sheet, strip, wire, extruded sections, etc., engineering designers are continuing to specify the copper metals for applications large and small. A number of uses of copper today are spectacular and impressive, such as the large copper brewing vats, but the majority are in the form of machine or plant components and are usually unobtrusive to the layman.

The vast chemical engineering industry, which affects almost every aspect of daily life, uses copper (or its alloys) as a constructional material because of its high rate of heat transfer, its ease of manipulation and joining and its resistance to certain corrosive acids at normal or moderately high temperatures. The choice of material often depends mainly upon the latter consideration which in turn involves not only the nature of the liquid concerned but also its temperature, concentration, rate of flow, etc. For very exacting conditions 'Monel', a nickel–copper alloy, is often specified.

Copper plate or sheet is ductile and malleable. It can readily be hammered into pans or shaped and riveted, brazed, or welded into tanks, boilers and other containers of all shapes and sizes. Very large thick boiling-pans are also made from aluminium brass. Copper and a wide range of alloys are fabricated into tubes for transporting a variety of liquids and gases, including oil products, and they are also used for heating coils and in evaporators, refrigerators (for which there is a special range of sizes), in shell and tube condensers and for numerous other purposes.

Copper evaporators are used for concentrating sugar, milk, extract of malt, coffee, tannin, and for gelatine, lactic acid, sulphite liquor, etc. The American nuclear power station at Indian Point has a giant evaporator, 65 ft long, in which the tube bundles are made of 80/20 cupro-nickel.

Other copper alloys, including silicon bronze and 'Monel', are employed in the evaporation of sea-water, an application which is expected to increase with current expansion in the construction of distillation plant.

Glucose converters, sugar rollers, stirrers, and furnace-pans, vacuum pans, stills, fruit-slicing wheels, cattle-food and poultry mashers, heat exchangers, textile-drying machines, and the rotproofing of textiles for damp tropical climates are among the many miscellaneous items for which copper and copper alloys are used.

Copper distilling columns used in the production of industrial alcohol, fatty acids, essential oils, etc., are of special interest. The great penicillin plant at Speke, near Liverpool, is a specific instance of the use of copper in this respect. The recovery of extracts calls for fractionating columns which are 23 ft high and 5 ft in diameter and are built of deoxidized copper sheets. Each column is in seven sections, six of which have riveted copper bubble plates, and each plate incorporates sixty copper bubblers and up-tubes. This makes an interesting comparison with the practice a thousand years ago of the Arabs who distilled essences in gourd-shaped copper vessels.

In the numerous operations involved in the brewing of beer, copper has played a predominant part for many centuries. Copper sheet is very often used for lining the mash tuns and fermenting vessels; and the brewing coppers are almost always made of copper, as indeed their name implies. The world-famous brewery of Guinness's in Dublin has nineteen of these huge coppers, each of which holds 23,400 gallons. The slotted false bottoms of brewery mash tuns are made of bronze or brass. The round or oval coiled tubes called attemperators, through which cold water or brine circulates in the fermenting vessels, are of copper because of its high heat conductivity, and so are the steam coils in the brewing copper and the various distribution pipes. Copper tanks may even carry the beer away.

In the allied industry dealing with the distilling of whisky and other alcoholic spirits, the initial operations somewhat resemble those for brewing, but more alcohol is produced and a different yeast is employed. The fermented liquor is distilled in either a fire- or steam-heated whisky-still (Fig. 59) or in a columnar rectifying still. All this plant is invariably made of copper, as are the tubular condensing coils.

In scores of other industries, which are loosely classified under general engineering, copper and copper alloys are used for an infinite variety of applications, ranging from small mass-produced parts in free-machining brass to equipment for the 'space-age' industries of rocket production and atomic energy. The giant electro-magnets employed in atom-smashers have copper wire windings. A cyclotron at Harwell has 70 tons of copper strip for this purpose, while 'Nimrod', a more recent machine at the same plant, has more than 300 tons of high-conductivity copper bars coiled around its electro-magnet. The proton synchrotron at Brookhaven, New York, which is even larger, can accelerate its bombarding particles up to 30,000 million electron-volts. The electro-magnet of this huge machine measures 843 ft across and contains about 4,000 tons of iron and 400 tons of copper bars in coils. All these giants have evolved from a small machine built in 1930. One of its most essential parts, the magnetron body, was turned wholly out of high-conductivity copper.

13. Agriculture and Horticulture

All over the world an incessant war is waged against animal diseases which attack cattle and sheep, and the fungus growths, moulds, microbes and insect pests that decimate crops. In this struggle many kinds of treatment are needed, for what is effective in some diseases may be quite useless in others. Spraying and dusting are the most common remedies, and copper compounds are a constituent of many of the powders and solutions used.

Much information on this vital subject will be found in the C.D.A. Publication No. 41, *Copper Compounds in Agriculture and Industrial Microbiology*, from which the following statement is taken:

'The earliest commercial use of copper was in the form of sulphate as a seed dressing to destroy cereal diseases. Much later it was discovered that copper sulphate also prevented foliage diseases. If applied in too strong a solution it damaged the foliage but, by mixing with lime, Bordeaux Mixture was formed, and this has excellent adherence to foliage. This mixture enables plants to be provided with a protective coating of copper which prevents the penetration of the spores into the tissues. As long as the copper deposit remains on the tissue protection is maintained.

The most serious disease treated in this manner is potato blight, and neglect to spray the crop can be disastrous. Tomatoes are also sprayed against blight, raspberries and currants against leaf-spot; also stone-fruits, hops and vines, citrus fruits, bananas, tea (against blister blight), coffee (for rust and blight), and tobacco (for wildfire).

Probably, about 200,000 tons of copper sulphate are used in the world every year for these and similar purposes, in addition to smaller quantities of other copper compounds such as copper oxide and oxychloride and the copper-arsenic compound known as Paris Green.

Minute quantities of copper are essential to life; hence it is the practice on poor peaty or sandy soils deficient in that element to add copper sulphate to the usual fertilizer, thereby increasing the yield of the crops. For similar reasons 'salt licks' are provided for sheep to prevent the disease of lambs known as 'sway-back', and for cattle and other grazing animals. The dangerous tropical disease of bilharzia, which is due to a minute animal parasitic on snails, is also controlled by treating infected streams and lakes with a copper sulphate solution. Liver rot in sheep, due to flukes in another water-snail, is also treated by applying copper sulphate to the infected ground.

Thus, in the 20th Century we have turned the complete circle. Industry began with man, the agriculturist, picking up shining pieces of copper and wondering what they were; and we conclude with man, the horticulturist, putting back the same element in solution out of a watering-can.

Bibliography

1. BROMEHEAD, C. E. N. Practical Geology in Ancient Britain. Pt. I: The Metals. *Proc. Geol. Ass., Lond.* (1947), **58**, 348–351.
2. Ibid., p. 352.
3. COGHLAN, H. H. *Notes on the Prehistoric Metallurgy of Copper and Bronze in the Old World* (1951), pp. 47–62. Oxford.
4. LUCAS, A. *Ancient Egyptian Materials and Industries* (1948).
5. PETRIE, J. FLINDERS. Ancient Egyptain Art. *Ency. Brit.* (1911), 11th Edn., Vol. 9 pp. 73, 74.
6. Ibid., p. 73.
7. SMITH, P. *Dictionary of Greek and Roman Biography and Mythology* (1844), Vol. 1, pp. 683–4.
8. SMITH, A. H. *Guide to the Greek and Roman Antiquities in the British Museum* (1912), p. 182.
9. VITRUVIUS, L. *De Architectura*, Trans. Granger, Vol. 2, Bk. VIII, c. 6, p. 189.
10. GOWLAND, H. Copper and its Alloys in Early Times (1912), *J. Inst. Met.* p. 43.
11. SMITH, R. A. *Guide to the Antiquities of the Bronze Age in the British Museum* (1920).
12. SCOTT, G. G. *Gleanings from Westminster Abbey* 1863.
13. BIRCH, G. H. *Trans. St. Paul's Ecclesiological Soc.* (1890), **2,** p. 111.
14. BRADLEY, E. T. *Annals of Westminster Abbey* (1898), p. 144.
15. HAMILTON, H. *The Early English Copper and Brass Industries to 1800* (1926), p. 344.
16. 34 & 35 Henry VIII, c. 6.
17. CITY OF LONDON. *Calendar of Letter Books* (1907, 1911), I, K, etc.
18. HAKLUYT, R. 1926 edn., **2,** p. 8.
19. SCOTT, G. G. Op cit., p. 93.
20. ALEXANDER, W. O. Development of the Copper, Zinc and Brass Industries in Great Britain from A.D. 1500 to 1900. *Murex Rev.* (1955), **1,** (15), p. 399.
21. Ibid, p. 408.
22. HAMILTON, H. Op. cit., p. 255.
23. MEDEYARD, E. *Life of Josiah Wedgwood* (1865), Vol. 1, p. 239.
24. SMILES, S. *Lives of the Engineers: Boulton and Watt* (1865), p. 396.
25. STURGEON, W. *Lectures on Electricity* (1841), p. 207.
26. FLEMING, J. A. Electricity, *Ency. Brit.* (1911), 11th Edn., Vol. 9, p. 182.
27. Ibid., p. 188.
28. THOMPSON, S. P. *Life of William Thomson, Lord Kelvin.*
29. NEUBURGER, A. *The Technical Arts and Sciences of the Ancients* (1930), p. 37.
30. LIDDELL, D. M. *Handbook of Non-Ferrous Metallurgy* (1945), pp. 149–151.

Many of the above contain considerable bibliographies.

Index

Acknowledgments

1, 2, 3, 5, 19	British Museum
4	Science Museum & University College, London
7, 8, 10, 12, 15, 16, 20, 22, 24, 25, 26, 30, 31, 32	Victoria & Albert Museum, London
9	Royal Ontario Museum
11	Japan Air Lines
13, 14	Federation of Nigeria
17	C.I.S.A.R., Italy
18	British Travel Association
23, 27, 28, 29, 33, 34, 36, 37, 40, 41, 42, 44	Science Museum, London
35	Royal Institution
38, 39	H.M. Postmaster General
43	Science Museum and Marconi Wireless Telegraph Co. Ltd.
45, 57	Associated Electrical Industries Ltd.
46	Campbell's Press Studios Ltd.
47	British Insulated Callender's Construction Co. Ltd.
48	Standard Telephones & Cables Ltd.
49, 50	R.S.T. Ltd.
51	John Laing & Son Ltd.
54	Outokumpu, Finland
55	British Insulated Callender's Cables Ltd.
56	John Brown & Co. (Clydebank) Ltd.
58	Bowater Organization
59	Distillers Co. Ltd.
60	Alan S. Marshall
61	Daniel Adamson & Co. Ltd.
62	Air Products Ltd.
63	I.M.I. (Kynoch) Ltd.
64	Morland Braithwaite Ltd.
65	Jean P. Rüegg